OPEN HEART CHICAGO

An Anthology of Chicago Writing

Vincent Francone

Editor

Blue Heron Book Works, LLC
Allentown, Pennsylvania

Yo, Scott!

Save this book!

It could be

worth #18 00)

Someday!

R.B. Mchugh

Table of Contents

Introduction

Not My Chicago

1.

In her pamphlet *I Dated Graham Greene*, Lucy Ellmann (Evanston, IL native, currently residing in Scotland) states that too many stories have already been set in Chicago. This doesn't stop her from telling a few Chicago stories herself. All due respect to Ellmann (hero!), but the authors represented in this collection, and me its humble editor, disagree.

Of course, there are Chicago stories that have been told too many times—the noirish stuff, the celebrations of poverty and political corruption posing as hard-hitting examinations, the myths (that poor scapegoated O'Leary cow), the Capone industry, the scrappy tales of a muscular city... yeah, yeah, yeah.

Truth: there's a bit of that romanticizing in here. Because there's a bit of that in Chicago. And while this anthology could've easily focused on gritty crime, I wanted it to represent as many aspects of this strange town as possible. To that end, I present fiction and nonfiction, different genres, different styles, different perspectives, seasoned pros and up-and-comers. Because that's what the city is: different neighborhoods full of different people somehow coexisting.

2.

I moved from the southwest suburbs to the north side of Chicago in 1993. Growing up, my impression of the city was formed by some of its most famous characters: Mike Royko, Nelson Algren, and Studs Terkel, sure, but also Steve Dahl and the Blues Brothers. Most of those visions of Chicago represented select generations (the Depression/WWII gang to the Boomers) and cultures (European immigrants and their children). They have too often taken control of the Chicago narrative. This book is not an attempt to rectify cultural hegemony so much as add to the stories previously told. Of course, a few of those Boomers got in (they're impossible to avoid). But that's okay— I wanted a mix of voices. I also wanted to skip the same tales you already know, be they from *The Man with the Golden Arm*, *Ferris Bueller's Day Off*, or the ongoing violence porn of cable news networks that love to describe my city as a war zone.

3.

Just after high school, my view of the city changed. No longer the home of the blues, Chicago became the location of a specific, trebly kind of music that I adored. Naked Raygun and Big Black, Ministry and Revolting Cocks and all those Wax Trax bands. I saw the city as a magic land of punk rock, late night cafés, dive bars, and hip bookstores— a culture that made sense to me. And then the 21st century arrived and a lot of that stuff was gone. My beloved secondhand bookshops and indie record stores vanished. The music changed. The neighborhoods changed. The buildings got torn down. New ones sprung up. I got a little grumpy about it all, even imagined a project called *Ghosts of Chicago* that would document a time when Wicker Park was a place to score heroin, not a place to find $20 bowls of ramen. Until I realized that everyone in this damn city feels this way about *their* time. How much better it used to be. How much everything has changed.

Chicago like every city is forever evolving. Looking at the writers in this anthology, one will notice that the city doesn't seem the same to each of them. (Most of us in this town can't agree which is the correct spelling: "the El" or "The el" or "the L"—the variances represented in different stories here.) My grandfather would not recognize the neighborhood where his first children were born, once a haven for Italian immigrants, now a hipster stronghold. My dad and my brother both get sentimental about Wrigley Field, even though—despite the tenacious ivy—it has changed as well. I'm sure Gen Z can't imagine a time before the Bean (as we call Cloud Gate, that is when we have to refer to the damn thing), but it still seems weird to me that this alien sculpture landed alongside Michigan Avenue. It's become iconic, I suppose, but it seems out of place. Not my Chicago.

4.

While I would've loved a Gen X ode to long-gone Xanadus like Lounge Ax or Medusa's, I'm thrilled by the selection of pieces here, among them Steve Trumpter's tale of dibs (and someone *had* to write about dibs) and Adrienne Gunn's discussion of childrearing in the big, stressful city; RL Gehringer's reminiscence of boyhood hijinks; Gary Slezak slowly understanding his father while toiling on his family's Christmas tree lot; Sandi Wisenberg's episodes along the CTA; Ines Bellina working out her 30s in a city more suited to pop culture fairytales than New York; Cajetan Sorich fighting class wars at an upscale spa; Nick Francone's tribute to Wrigley Field; Wayne Lerner's tale of a boyhood trip to Comiskey Park; and Christopher Sebela's meditation on Chicago's drunken, overzealous sports fans. I present comedy (Joe Mallon), tragedy (Dipika Mukherjee), lyricism (Rose Woodson), nostalgia (Anthony Ball), surrealism (Lorena Ornelas), and a few less classifiable bits (Jeremey T. Wilson, Vojislav Pejović, Nancy Poling) because Chicago is hard to pare down into one thing. Ever-changing, a place where I've had both my best and worst days, a source of steady frustration and occasional joy. Different things to the different people who have landed on these shores, a tiny fraction of them given voice in these pages, some established writers, others published for the first time. Because, there is no one Chicago. There's mine, there's yours. And yours is not my Chicago, and that's okay. It's a city for all of us, different in so many ways, good and bad.

Vincent Francone

Dibs *Steve Trumpeter*

My husband Jacob is snoring on an air mattress in the bedroom, and our five-year-old is sitting in the middle of our hardwood floor squeezing Play-Doh between his fingers. All his other toys are packed away. We each have one change of clothes in an unsealed box in the hall by the bathroom and some toiletries on the sink, but outside of that, this apartment is as bare as the day we moved in, before Samuel was even born. The space haunts me, empty and uncluttered as it is, the counters and floors scrubbed clean like a crime scene, except for the spots where Samuel has mashed Play-Doh between the slats.

From the upstairs apartment, I hear Mrs. Finelli clomp across the kitchen in her cupboard-rattling way. Jacob and I liked to make mafia jokes about her cement shoes—a little on-the-nose, perhaps, given the way she speaks of her ex-husband—but the footsteps never really bothered me. I've always found the sounds of my neighbors comforting. The low infra-sonics of their TVs, wall-dampened conversations, even squeaky bedsprings and climactic moans served as proof that I inhabited a society. Tonight, there is strident purpose in her heavy steps as she scoots all the way from the kitchen to the living room turret windows at the front of the building. I hear her throw open the window and shout out to the street.

"You can't park there!" she screams. "That's my spot! It's reserved."

I peer out my own window and see two young dudebros in puffy, oversized jackets standing on the curb next to a pair of folding chairs they've tossed into a snowdrift on the sidewalk. There is a BMW parked where Mrs. Finelli's spot should be, right in front of the U-Haul moving truck we've rented that holds all the accumulated things that once made this apartment a home.

"Sit and spin, lady," the short one says, holding up a middle finger.

"It's a public street."

"That's my spot," she yells again, but the men just head up the block, laughing at her.

Mrs. Finelli has her own son who still lives with her. He's in his early 20's—a sweet enough kid who always looks after our plants when we're out of town—but he's also kind of a dipshit. Ostensibly, he attends junior college studying Computer Science and works evenings in a vape shop in Logan Square. As far as his facility with computers goes, from what I've heard through the ceiling, it mostly consists of jerking off to internet porn while his mother is at church in the mornings. His other obsession is his Honda, which casts a neon purple glow on the pavement and sits a few inches off the ground with its tires cambered at such a tilt that the car looks perpetually knock-kneed. When we got a foot and a half of snow dumped on us last week, his mother waited for the snowplows to rumble through, then spent two hours digging that Honda out for him while he slept in, just so he wouldn't be late to work. After he left, she dragged two folding chairs into the spot to claim dibs. And while it's been five days since the snow has fallen, it hasn't melted yet, putting us well into the gray area of an unwritten Chicago statute that seems to revel in its fluid interpretation.

The door upstairs slams and startles Samuel, followed by the rumble of Mrs. Finelli bounding down the stairs. Samuel is grimacing at the taste of his red Play-Doh. "That stuff's not food," I say for the hundredth time. "Come here." He spits out the Play-Doh into my hand. "Stay and watch this with me," I say. Mrs. Finelli marches out to the curb and shouts up the street, shaking her fist like a cartoon character.

Samuel rubs his tongue with the palm of his hand to get the taste out of his mouth. "Waff haffewing?" he asks.

"We're going to make one last memory of the city you were born in," I say. Perhaps this isn't very good mothering on my part, but I want him to have this last image of city living.

He hugs my leg and peers out the window from behind me, as if he might get in trouble for spying. "Don't be such a 'fraidy cat," I say. "Watch."

In Chicago, dibs might be an unwritten rule, but the consequences are clear. You violate the rules, you risk your tires, your windows, your paint job. Mrs. Finelli looks up and down the street, as if she's searching for witnesses to share her outrage, but there's no one out tonight. She picks up a chair, and I hold my breath and scratch Samuel's back like I do when he's been crying for reasons he can't express. "Here we go," I whisper.

But Mrs. Finelli only folds up the chair and leans it against the tree in her planter. Samuel lets go of my leg and returns to his spot on the floor, exhaling like he's escaped a doctor visit without any shots. I squeeze Samuel's spit-slimy glob of Play-Doh like a stress ball and watch Mrs. Finelli drag her folding chairs back to the apartment building, muttering impotent curses in her mother tongue.

We are moving to Naperville so Samuel can go to a good school. That's what Jacob says, anyway. The Chicago Public School system is a gamble, he says, and the odds aren't good. He drives our boy to Spanish lessons twice a week and reads to him every night before bed. There are piano lessons and "li'l yogi" yoga classes. Every Thursday, we all go out to dinner together and Jacob makes a lesson out of Ethiopian cuisine or sushi or Dutch-Indonesian fusion. But there are times like right now, as I watch Samuel switch to the blue Play-Doh and make that lemon-wedge face all over again, when I wonder what lessons he really needs. Does this boy honestly require every single academic advantage humanly possible? Are we laying claim to something to which we have no right?

"That stuff's not food," I say for the hundred and first time.

The air mattress is only a full-sized bed rather than the California King that's waiting for us in Naperville, and my husband has put on a few since I married him, so I give Samuel the spot next to Jacob and resign myself to his Thermarest in the living room. I'll be up all night anyway, despite being worn out from a day spent carrying box after box down two flights of stairs. I'll grind my teeth to the sounds of Mrs. Finelli pacing angrily around her living room while her kid circles the block in futile search of a legal parking spot. I know she's mad that she chickened out, and I'm ashamed to admit I'm a little embarrassed for her, too.

Jacob's keys are on the bench by the turret window along with the contents of his pockets. He already has the Metra pass that will get him downtown and back each day tucked into the plastic sleeve that houses his work ID. "It's only 35 minutes if I catch the express," he says. I used to bike to work, but now I'm going to freelance part-time from home, at least for the next couple of months while we "test out the transition," as my supervisor puts it, unwilling to admit she's going to whittle down my assignments until I transition into a stay-at-home mom. Our new place is only ten minutes from the grocery store, though the realtor means by car, not by foot. And because we'll have a heated driveway—O wonders of suburban technology!—I'll never have to shovel out a parking space again.

Samuel sucks his thumb while he sleeps, and I try to imagine him someday using a key to etch a dick into the paint job of a BMW that some asshole parked in his rightful spot.

The next morning, when Jacob wakes up, he says I look tired and loads Samuel into the Odyssey that's filled with the fragile things we can't trust to the U-Haul. He wants to get one last breakfast at the brunch spot on the corner, but I tell them to go ahead without me. I'll get a head start in the truck and meet them at our new house.

I walk through the apartment, saying goodbye to each tiny room, and though I want to go upstairs and give Mrs. Finelli a big hug before I leave, her son is home, and I don't feel comfortable interrupting their morning. I go downstairs and climb into the truck, and from this height, the snow doesn't look so deep. The BMW from last night is still parked in Mrs. Finelli's spot, and as I pull out, I make sure to run the truck's front bumper along the length of the car's passenger side. The reverberating screech of metal on metal rings in my ears long after I hit the traffic on the Tri-State tollway near the exit to the towns with names I'll soon have to learn.

Little Man *Jeremy T. Wilson*

My father came back to me as a bobble head. I was getting ready for work and there he was in my closet beside the box of old bobble heads that used to line the windowsill of his office. When I was eleven, he coached my little league team and custom ordered bobble heads of all the players and coaches. They looked nothing like us, but they had our names and numbers on the back, and each was positioned in some dramatic baseball action. In his bobble head likeness, my father leaned on a baseball bat, right foot crossed over left. The back of his jersey said "Dad" above the number 1. He'd been dead for over a year.

"Hi, Little Man," he said, "I'd like to celebrate with you today."

At first, I didn't know what he was talking about, but then I remembered it was the day of the Chicago Cubs victory parade. I hadn't planned on going. That little league team was the last time I cared about baseball.

"I've got to go to work," I told him.

"Work? You think this kind of thing happens every day?"

I picked him up. His eyes were not the dead eyes of a bobble head, but watery and blue, like the lake, like mine. I missed seeing how proud they could be of me.

We squeezed on the El with the rest of the city, everyone smiling and holding open beers like the law no longer applied. I kept my father in the front pocket of my hoodie, but I could hear his muffled complaints about how hot it was and how he hadn't come all this way not to see, so I took him out and held him close to my chest like an ice cream cone. He smiled and bobbed his head along with the rhythm of the train, but now he complained it was too crowded and that he couldn't see out the window. I told him he'd seen it all a million times. Nothing had changed.

"Why don't you spend some time dead and then tell me there's nothing to see," my father said.

We followed the crowd down to Grant Park, to the end of the parade route. All the people made it difficult to get close, so I held my father high in the air like a torch so he could see the ceremony projected on the big screens and listen to the speeches. My arm got tired. When it was over, and the players hoisted the gold trophy, "Go Cubs Go" blasted through the speakers. I got caught up in the moment and pretended my father's head was a microphone and sang the words I remembered into his cap.

"Your breath stinks," he said.

We scoured the souvenir shops looking for World Series gear, but most of the stores had already been cleaned out, nothing but baseballs banging around galvanized buckets, a few keychains and bumper stickers. At the last store we went to, my father made me buy a pair of decals, white with a blue W, a replica of the flag that flies above the scoreboard after a Cubs' win. My father flew the same flag off the front of our house all season, win or lose. When the clerk wasn't looking, my father told me to stick each of the decals over a mannequin's bare breasts.

"Winners," he said. "Just like Melinda. I want to see Melinda. Text her."

Melinda told me to meet her at a wine bar near her gym because she had yoga that afternoon. I set my father on top of the table next to my water glass. He told me he'd like a California zinfandel. The glass he wanted cost eighteen dollars. "You can't even drink," I said.

"I can smell."

I told him I didn't want to pay eighteen dollars for him to smell a glass of wine.

"Who's the dead guy, here?"

I ordered the wine.

I remembered the way the room smelled after Melinda had come to see my father for the last time, after I'd helped her by taking my mother to the movies, convincing her it was a good idea to get out of the house for a while. I told the hospice nurse a friend of my father's from work was coming by. My mother cried through the whole movie even though it was supposed to be funny. I felt sorry for her, guilty for what I'd done, what I knew. I listened to her cry while another woman sat by her husband's side, stroking his cheek, wetting his lips with ice chips. When we got home, I could smell Melinda's perfume in my parents' room. It was spicy and exotic, not like my mother's rosy aroma. It smelled like another language.

Today she had her yoga mat strapped to her shoulder, and she was wearing a white zip-front hoodie, not fully zipped. I waved and she came over. She stood for a second with her arms out, expecting me to stand up and hug her, but when I didn't, she sat down, the full glass of wine in front of her.

"Is this a California zin?" she asked.

My father and I both nodded.

"Get me closer," my father said.

I pushed him closer. Melinda looked down at him, then up at me. "How about the Cubs?" she said. "Your father would've been beside himself." She flicked his cap, and his head went wild.

"She's got a ring on her finger," my father said.

She caught me looking at the ring and splayed her fingers on her chest, showing off the diamond. "I'm getting married," she said.

"Tell her I wish things could've been different for us. That we had more time."

"He wishes things could've been different," I said.

"Oh, he does?" She laughed and picked him up and held him in her left hand. "What else does he say?"

"Tell her I miss her."

"He misses you."

She turned him around so she could see the back of his jersey and lifted him close to her ear. "I can't hear him," she said.

"Ask her to go back to your place and take a bath with you."

"Would you like to take a bath with me?" I said it, but I didn't feel like I was the one saying it, and after I said it, I wasn't certain I had.

Melinda set my father down on the table. "Would you like the number of my therapist?" she asked.

I reached for my father, and when I did, I knocked over the wine glass and spilled red wine all over her. She jumped out of her chair and took off her hoodie. She wore a black, athletic tank top underneath, the straps crisscrossed over her muscular back.

A waitress came over and handed her a wad of napkins. "I can get you another," she said.

Tears gathered in my father's blue eyes. "She's already got another," he said. "Let's go, Little Man."

He asked me if I'd take him to a strip club. I told him sure, but instead we got on the El and rode it to my mother's house in the burbs, what had been their house together, our house. The white W flag was still flying out front. "You tricked me, Little Man." I shoved him in the front pocket of my hoodie. "Now wait just a second, Little Man." I pressed my thumb against his grinning mouth.

My mother was surprised to see me, but she wasn't busy. Lately she'd been thinking about moving to Florida where my aunt lived. I knew she wanted to sell the house. It was too big for her all by herself, and she said she still felt like she had a lot of life left to live, and it would be fine with her to live that life without winter.

"Don't leave," I said.

"I haven't decided."

"Please stay."

I hugged my mother, and she felt the bobble head in my pocket. I pulled it out, my thumb still covering his mouth. "He wants to say he's sorry."

"Never too late for that," she said.

I thought about taking my thumb off his mouth so I could hear those words for myself, but he'd said enough. I tightened my grip and ripped his head off. He didn't come back again.

Inherently Chaotic *Adrienne Gunn*

"How does Max cope with his anxiety?" my son's psychiatrist asked me the summer Max turned 9.

"He draws a circle on the gym floor and sits in the middle, and then all the other kids have to stay outside of the circle."

She considered this. "We'd like him feeling better than that."

No shit, I wanted to say. But I just smiled ruefully because, well, here we are, and what can you do? And obviously I wanted her to know I'm a good mother.

I don't remember a time that I wasn't living with an anxious person. When I was a kid, my mother was always worried. If we were on a family trip, she'd wait until we were about an hour outside of town and then start wondering aloud if she'd locked the door or turned off the curling iron. And then she and my father would tersely debate whether or not to turn our Oldsmobile around, and I could feel the tension rising, rising, as I gripped the backseat's velour upholstery. Later, when I was an adult, she once told me, "Today I will be practicing HALT. It stands for 'hungry, angry, lonely, tired.' I will alert you when I feel one of those things."

Perhaps it was this sort of training that prompted me to marry (and later divorce) an anxious man, the kind of man who needs to take a Xanax before entering a Trader Joe's. Which, in theory, is not an entirely irrational reaction to Trader Joe's, but this is just one example. You'll have to trust me that the others paint him as less adorably neurotic.

I've considered the possibility that there are two types of people in the world: the anxious and those who take care of them. I've been addressing other people's anxiety for so long that I've become infinitely reasonable, flexible, and accommodating, and so, really, it should not have been a surprise when I found myself the mother of an anxious child. It was the ultimate promotion.

When Max was 3, after I'd divorced his father, the two of us moved to Chicago from Oregon where I'd been working on my master's in creative writing. Max was a sweet kid who loved to dance and jump around at the park and read stories about animals. I took him on a lot of hikes when we lived in Oregon, first carrying him on my back and later holding his hand. I remember fresh air and clear skies and rocky paths and have a mental picture of him toddling down a slope of tall grass, laughing. I don't remember him being anxious then, but surely he must have been. Or at least the seeds were there.

We settled in a two-flat in North Center, and as I assembled his bookcases, I was filled with a lot of glossy ideas about all the high-culture things he would get to do as a kid growing up in the big city. Me? I grew up in Rockford, which was fine, especially if you like strip malls, but not really an exhilarating place that entire novels are written about. Obviously Max and I would expand our minds at all of Chicago's museums. Most likely we'd become members of Lincoln Park Zoo — a lot of my friends from college already were. By the time he was 5, he'd know about feminism, systemic racism, the patriarchy, genderqueer, and genderfuck, and he'd be eating sushi and appreciating musical theater and possibly learning to sail.

If I'm being honest, I was very smug.

Max started preschool in Roscoe Village, and the very first week, his teacher called me to report that he was under a bush. I was confused. What was I supposed to do about it? I was at work. I remember hanging up the phone baffled and then writing the whole thing off as one of those weird passive-aggressive preschool things, like when your kid has an accident and they literally send the shit-filled pants home in a plastic bag. Later I understood that the teacher had wanted me to think of this moment as the first real indication that Max wasn't going to be easy, that he was going to be a kid with very little chill, that he was going to be the kid under a bush, or a table, or later walking out the classroom door and wandering the halls.

As Max got older, his anxiety got worse — slowly at first and then sort of all at once. We did try to do all of the Chicago things I'd imagined, but I quickly found that a crowded Field Museum would rattle him so much that he'd completely shut down, becoming sort of a zombie, and even when he was back in the car, cruising along Lake Shore Drive, it would take him a while to reenter himself. And then he'd be apologetic and embarrassed, and I'd feel terrible because he was only 5 years old, so what did he have to apologize for?

And then I'd worry.

When your kid has too much anxiety to do drop-off birthday parties or sleepovers or playdates with more than two kids, or when your friends raising kids who aren't exceptionally difficult invite you to things like the Pride Parade or Burger Fest or the zoo and you know the amount of pep-talking it will take to get your kid there, and how as soon as you're there, he'll complain of a headache or a stomachache or clutch at you or not respond to the other kids at all—you worry. I chewed my nails over how small his world was going to be. Before going to sleep at night, I thought about how, at home, he was one person—funny, joyful, thoughtful—and how as soon as we left our apartment, no one saw any of that. And there was so much explaining. "Max is difficult," I would say, but still it didn't seem like people really understood the cost-benefit calculus involved in dragging him to something like a Phish show at Wrigley Field— that was my ex-husband, obviously, I would never take an anxious child to see a band whose songs literally never end.

Cities are inherently chaotic. That's part of the magic. And anxiety is about control. About seizing control over your environment to feel calm. Max's anxiety has made me think a lot about who the city is for. If you're a kid who finds a lot of stimuli stressful—what then? Is the city just not for you?

I'm not ready to believe that. Max is 10 now, and I want to give him the coping mechanisms he needs to take advantage of everything Chicago, and the world, has to offer. So, we see a psychiatrist until we get the medication right. We say no to street fests. We arrive at the Shedd Aquarium 15 minutes before it opens so we're the first people in the door. We never go on weekends and holidays. We drive instead of taking the train. We limit the amount of time we're going to be there and schedule breaks. It's a pain in the ass, really, but that's parenting, I'm told. That's life.

I have this photo of Max at the aquarium, staring up at a beluga whale that's staring back down at him. A stream of light shines through the water, illuminating his face, and it's a perfect picture, really, the kind you'd see in a magazine. And there it is. All the hassle and stress are worth it because you know I put that shit on my Instagram. But really, what Max has taught me about motherhood is this: The dreams change. They're never what you think they're going to be. But then you change. And there's beauty in that too.

Ketchup *A. L. Trellis*

Characters:

Bill (middle-aged, portly)

Harold (shabby, thin, homeless, distraught)

Scene:

Northwest corner of Pratt and Glenwood, Rogers Park neighborhood, far north side of Chicago, Illinois.

Scene One

Harold is sitting on a milk crate near a convenience store. He has a cup in his right hand and is shaking it slowly, the few coins inside making a jingling sound. Bill approaches the store.

Harold:

Spare some change?

Bill:

Sorry, I never carry cash.

Harold:

Anything'll help, please.

Bill:

Sorry. [*Gets ready to walk into the store, pauses*] Wait—what about this: can I buy you something?

Harold:

Oh, that'd be great.

Bill:

Something to eat?

Harold:

Yes, please. Maybe a hot dog?

Bill:

A hot dog it is.

Harold:

They have a two-for-two-dollars deal, I think.

Bill:

Very well—two hot dogs. Anything to drink?

Harold:

A coke?

Bill:

You got it. [*Enters the store.*]

Scene Ends

*****

Scene Two

Harold is as before. Bill exits the convenience store holding a bag. He approaches Harold.

Bill:

Here you are—two hot dogs and a coke. I got you a brownie as well.

Harold:

Thanks, mister. You know, some people think I just want money so I can buy drugs, but I never did drugs in my life. I'm just unlucky. Okay, I've made some mistakes, but I only ask for help because I need it. I'm just hungry. Really, I can't thank you enough.

Bill:

I believe you.

Harold:

You're a good person.

Bill:

Well…

Harold:

Really, you are. [*Opens the bag*] And look… mustard and everything! Oh, is there any ketchup?

Bill:

Excuse me?

Harold:

Do they have any ketchup?

Bill:

[*Incredulous*] For the *hot dogs?*

Harold:

Yes.

Bill:

You're telling me you want to put ketchup ON A HOT DOG!

Harold:

[*Tentative*] Um… yeah. That's how I like 'em.

Bill:

Oh no. [*Takes back the bag of food*] There's no way I'm letting you put ketchup on a hot dog.

Harold:

What?

Bill:

Buddy, in case you don't know where you are, this is CHICAGO. Have you ever heard of anyone in this town defiling a hot dog with ketchup? What kind of a sick monster would put that crap on a hot dog? Even a hot dog from a convenience store deserves better. No, there's no way I'm going to sit here and let you commit the most egregious of culinary sins.

Harold:

But... that's how I eat them.

Bill:

That's disgusting! You make me SICK!

Harold:

I'm sorry... can I... please?

Bill:

[*Walking away*] Sorry, pal. Nothing I can do for you. [*Exits*]

Harold sits looking forlorn. The sky darkens over him, gradually engulfing the stage until all we see is Harold's silhouette. Sobbing is audible.

Curtain

You Are Here   *Anne-Marie Akin*

I wonder if the Chicago Transit Authority still distributes little folded maps? Now there are apps, but when I first came here, we had printed maps: paper and ink. People used to hang them on their walls as art. This was back when the Brown Line was still called the Ravenswood, at least in common parlance. This was when we used little gold coins to ride the train, little golden tokens about the size of dimes, which could take you downtown to a temp job or an audition. I think they cost around ninety cents.

I would unfold my map every night and study it, taking care to be gentle with the creases. In my mind's eye I watched the Ravenswood as it jogged lazily northwest, headed mysteriously beyond the Western borders of my world. After Rockwell, it didn't even trouble to be elevated. It was just a regular train.

The Red Line blazed or sauntered, depending on whether you were on an express or not. If you boarded an express to Howard when all you wanted was to go from Belmont up to Irving Park, you had a chance to rehearse the five stages of grief. Denial hit around Addison. Anger, Irving Park. Bargaining was Bryn Mawr. Depression, Morse. And acceptance, as you trudged resignedly down the stairs at Howard and crossed to the southbound tracks.

There were A trains and B trains, the two indistinguishable, as they both smelled like piss. If you got on an A but needed a B stop, you would watch helplessly out the window, reading SHERIDAN or MONTROSE as you flew past. There were no cell phones to call ahead and say you were going to be late.

And if you don't know Chicago, these names mean nothing to you, which is what they meant to me when I stared at the CTA map. This was a long time ago, when everything about Chicago was unknown to me, thrilling but also scary.

And now I have lived here for more than half my life, a quarter of a century, and I know my way all over this segregated, divided city, even South and West. Although I am a Northsider, I know Lawndale and Pilsen and Little Village, I know South Shore and Grand Boulevard and Bronzeville, Jefferson Park and Mayfair, I know lakefront and the West Side, and I never get lost. Why doesn't it feel like my home?

I will help you draw a map of Chicago. First, learn that east is always The Lake. Lake Michigan is a body of fresh water so big you can see it from space. I could find Chicago from the moon, looking down. I could find Chicago tucked along that bottom left-hand corner of Lake Michigan, but still it would not be my home.

I know it as well as the fretboard of my guitar. I know it better than Memphis, my hometown, or Atlanta, or Milwaukee. Yet I feel haphazardly placed, like a single curbside glove at the end of winter. I have lived here longer than anywhere else, I even owned a house here, but I always have my shoes by the front door waiting for the day when I leave. And when I leave, I will have an excellent sense of direction.

So, if you want to find yourself, and you are in Chicago, and not on the moon looking down, and you do not have a folded paper map in your pocket, you don't need to pull out a cell phone. You have only to lift your nose to the air and sniff for the Lake. If you can smell it, you are very far East, unless it is one of those spring days when the winds blow funny, and you can smell the lake all the way to Kedzie. Which is to say, you can smell fish and a faint watery greenness where normally you smell diesel fumes.

But even if you can't smell it, you can find it if you look and squint in a certain way. You can see that the buildings don't go on forever; there is some sudden vast openness in the distance. Say to yourself, "Aha, that is East." Turn your body so that the right side of you matches the Lake side of the city. Now you are facing North. Once you know where north is, you can draw a map in your head.

"Yes, yes, that's all fine and good," you are probably saying to me, "but I don't know how far north or south I am!"

Patience. I will help you. Learn the numbers of the streets. Every street runs consistently North-South or East-West, never wavering. You can trust a Chicago street.[1] For instance, Cermak is 2200 South. Damen is 2000 West, Foster 5200 North (Amundsen High School). Madison and State are neutral: 0 north and south (that street preacher on his milk crate). Unlike Atlanta, where the major thoroughfares meander in languid loops, so that you may find yourself at age twenty-one driving in hot, blinding circles, weeping at the corner of Peachtree and Peachtree, wondering if you're ever going to understand anything about the world.

Chicago is a grid, with only a handful of exceptions. It is a stolid, Midwestern city. No winding or curlicues. Once you learn the numbers, you can map out your life with ease. You can add important memories to your map. For example, I had my all-time favorite kiss in the front seat of a car parked around 3800 North, on that funny street in the park, east of Lakeshore Drive. It's called Recreational Drive. My second-favorite kiss was also pretty far East, just a little west of the inner drive, on a park bench near North Avenue. Both my daughters were born 5200 north, 2600 west; they were conceived on an angle street, about 3800 north, at a feminist health clinic above a modern dance studio.

If Chicago were entirely a grid, during rush hour we would be trapped in an embrace none of us want. And so the city planners, in their infinite wisdom, left us a handful of diagonal streets that bisect the city at an angle, giving us the confusing three-way intersection. These are the old Native pathways. If you are on one of these streets, such as Ogden, and you are a newcomer to Chicago, GET OFF. You will only get lost.

Lake Michigan tugs at my compass needle. Chicago offered me East instead of North. And if The Lake is on my left-hand side, then I know where my family is. I see the coordinates plotted like spokes or sunbeams, extending out from The Lake. My sweetheart: southeast near the Ohio/Kentucky border. My father and brother: south and a little west of me, along the Mississippi River. My apartment: 2100 W/6200 N; my former partner and the house we owned together: 4300 W. Our children are safely tucked away in school not too far from The Lake, across the street from the apartment I lived in when I was much, much younger than I am now (4300 N). This city

---

[1] We will not speak here about Wacker Drive, or its Stygian mirror, Lower Wacker.

I love is not quite my home, but it has given me a map, dependable as gravity. And above my head, a little arrow, and a sign: You Are Here.

The Christmas War   *Gary Slezak*

Whoever said "war is hell" should have added "so is Christmas." That would have made more sense of my father's life or given it some ironic justice. And it may have made more sense of my early life, when on top of a trailer late one Christmas Eve, I experienced my first moments of transcendence.

In World War II my father fought in the 14th Armored Division, crossed the bridge at Remagen, and entered Dachau just days after liberation. Weeks later he celebrated the Allied victory in a Munich beer hall, before spending eight months in Germany as part of the Allied Occupation. When he returned home to the South Side of Chicago on Christmas Eve, 1945, he was suffering from a great fatigue. He wore his uniform day and night, talked to no one, and refused to leave his parent's house.

Gradually, he snapped out of it and returned to his old supervisor's job at the stockyards, then left suddenly to buy a tavern with his war bonds. Later that year and just as suddenly, he rented a vacant lot and with his younger brother began a seasonal business that would last nearly half a century. One block long and one block wide, from the street to the alley, it was known as the North Woods, the largest Christmas tree lot on the South Side.

Its heyday enveloped my youth, from the mid-fifties to the early seventies, when everybody bought a Christmas tree. And its heyday shaped my life. For working with my father each December became an observance of something partly concealed, a reliving of the past. To my father that lot was more than just a place to instill the values of hard work. There was something from the war he was settling out there.

To the east was the Back of the Yards, to the west a broken-down airport. Two blocks south were the headquarters of the American Nazi Party. And in the middle stood an open lot.

It was the day after Thanksgiving. In a cold rain, my father, uncle, brother, and I began to dig hundreds of holes into the late November ground to support rows and rows of pipe that would hold each tree. Splashed to the eyebrows in mud, we positioned each pipe, hammered it down, and packed it with wet earth. While my uncle bent down with a yardstick and measured the rows, my father, dressed in his World War Two fatigues, began to rib my uncle about his perfectionist methods.

"What are ya doing down there, looking for land mines?" he asked, encouraging his sons to laugh with him.

My uncle, dressed in his Korean War outfit, looked up with a poker face and reported that the rows were uneven, and the holes would have to be dug again. It was a scene I had witnessed many times before: two brothers, opposites, competing for space on the same battlefield. An argument always followed. After a long silence my father would look up at the sky and intone to my uncle: "We're losing the light. If you wanna recreate the world and its holes, you're on your own. The rest of us are gonna keep digging."

And we did. Even in the dark.

"This should be a lesson to you two," my father lectured from his shovel.

"What have I always told ya? Get an education! So ya don't end up like me, working with my hands."

The sentiment was sincere, but the self-pity was staged. My father loved working with his hands—building shelves, painting walls, tarring his roof and driveway. He also loved to discount his younger brother's education. My uncle had gone to college, my father had quit high school to work in the stockyards. He even liked to poke fun at my uncle's Korean War service with comments like, "Would be the college boy who gets the shorter war."

Next came putting up the shack, a homemade contraption of wooden panels and boards, nailed shut and topped with a canvas roof, the only shelter from the approaching South Side winter. While the others mounted ladders to string light bulbs around the lot, I sullenly hammered the post of Santa's mailbox into the ground, then pounded down signs reading: NO DEER HUNTING and REINDEER CROSSING.

I was fourteen that year and had worked the lot since I was seven. There was something about the South Side that made one distrust Christmas, something almost novelistic in its pursuit of big dumb gods. And that year I could think of nothing bigger or dumber than that lot. Why was each December a month of combat? I felt enlisted in somebody else's war.

Which wasn't convenient at all, as I was waging a war with my libido. As a freshman at Brother Rice High School, I found myself not only attracted to girls across the fence at Mother McAuley, but to boys in my own class. I didn't know such a thing was possible in human experience and I felt doomed. I needed this lot like a hole in the head.

As my father and uncle began to argue about the straightness of the lights, my brother and I slumped against the side of the shack and discussed how not in the mood we were for maneuvers scheduled the next morning. To the north were the train yards.

Everything centered on the train yards now, for that is where the balsam would come: 3,400 in two boxcars from Nova Scotia. With a rented U-Haul tied to my father's '64 Ford station wagon, we'd pull out of the driveway of the family grocery store at dawn. My father had designed the store and the house himself. I remember him describing the plans to the architect: "Four levels. It's a pillbox in a sense." Indeed it was; the only thing it lacked was gun emplacements.

Off we'd go down Western Avenue, past Evergreen Plaza and Dan Ryan Woods, past a mile stretch of new and used car lots to the White Castle on 71st, then three miles further to the train yards at 51st and Central Park. Sweating in several layers of clothing, I sat silently, pissed and vaguely fearful of the territory we were entering: Marquette Park, my father's old neighborhood, a land of working-class whites and neo-Nazi youth.

Once at the train yards, my brother would be sent to get the stationmaster to come and open the padlock on the boxcar door. Shuffling like an old Russian in a Chekhov story, the stationmaster would join us in pushing and shoving and sliding open the vast iron door. Even I was enlivened by the sight and smell. There they were: 1,700 trees, tied in bundles, an entire boxcar packed from top to bottom. And behind this boxcar? Another boxcar.

And now it was my turn. Twenty feet above one could see a tiny crawl space not more than three feet high between the top of the trees and the roof of the boxcar. My father would back up the U-Haul as close to the boxcar as possible and shout to me:

"Well, let's go, Flash. Get up there!"

I would brace my foot on top of the U-Haul and lurch into the mountain of embedded trees, climb slowly to the top and roll over into the crawl space.

"Good, good," my father shouted. "Now, find the first piece of the puzzle!"

Slowly I would investigate the placement of the bundles and find the spot where they would all untangle. I'd grab the end of a bundle, turn it, then point it downward to my father. Soon the trailer was bursting with balsam and the boxcar became less filled. I would slowly and ever so cautiously stand. At this point, it never failed, my father would look up and bellow:

"What did I tell ya *last* year? Don't *step* on the branches!"

To which I would yell back, more vehemently each year:

"How in hell do you expect me to…"

"Alright, alright, just…don't!" he'd yell back.

My brother grinned annoyingly from below. Soon the roles would be reversed; he would replace me on top of the trees. Sweating bullets in the cold, shouting amid the roar of the trains, we would fill the trailer to the brim, close the boxcar door and make one journey back to the lot.

For three days and three nights, back and forth, in the rain and in the snow: a cortege of balsam moving slowly, promenading. Past the bungalows and two flats and my father's grade school. Past the plastic Santas and choirboys on the lawns. Past the lugubrious front of Becvar's Funeral Parlor (where we were stopped by a cop one night and given a ticket for the tail light that was out). Past the imposing facade of St. Gall Church at 55th and Sawyer, then Talman Federal Bank on Kedzie (the real place of family worship). Past the neighbors moving under the streetlights with tired, half-interested smiles. Past the taverns and bakeries, VFW hall, gas stations and muffler shops, the open lots, and finally to our lot, the North Woods.

Then unloading each haul, carrying the bundles to positions in piles around the back perimeter of the lot. If my brother dropped his end too soon, I lost my foothold in the snow or uneven ground and went flying into the air. One minute laughing, the next cursing as I tripped on the butt of a protruding trunk or chunk of ice. Slipping, sliding, falling with the bundle on top of me, a comic Stations of the Cross.

Back and forth for three days, in the mud or in the snow. But always, always the needles, everywhere. Inside our clothes, in our shoes, inside our socks, in the cuffs of our pants, inside our pants, needles creeping into the collar behind our necks, even in our ears. Until finally, the last boxcar was empty, its heavy iron doors closed. One almost forgot about tomorrow: maneuvers on the Eastern Front. Hundreds of scotch pine would arrive in trucks from Saugatuck, Michigan.

By mid-December the lot was teeming with ethnic hordes. The alley and street front were packed with cars and a major traffic jam occurred on Saturdays when next door the synagogue emptied out. Like newly trained soldiers, hundreds of trees stood at attention in rusty iron pipes. Everywhere people were filing into the rows of trees. Young couples, old couples, families together, even a local motorcycle gang, their bikes parked behind the shack. Children and dogs were running and playing in the snow. If someone opened Santa's mailbox, they would find three unmatched gloves and a handsaw.

Shouting from each row in different Eastern European dialects, the customers took stock of our bohemian camp. Wives and husbands haggled over the geometry of a Christmas tree.

"That's too short!"

"That's too bare!"

"It's cold out here, goddammit!"

"It's just going against a wall!"

Others haggled with my uncle, often shouting over the roar of airplanes:

"You got this thing for nothing out of the forest!"

"Lady, I lost my shirt bringing you this masterpiece!"

As the customers poured into every row, sizing up the stock, my father cut more bundles loose and tossed the trees to us as we ran to fill the empty pipes. On weekends and evenings there were a hundred customers at a time. And the one salesman, my uncle, dressed in his Korean War fatigues and an orange Cossack hat, was hard to miss.

"SEE ANYTHING YOU LIKE JUST CALL OUT!" he'd thunder into the rows.

"ALL TOP QUALITY CANADIAN BALSAM, SHIPPED BY RAIL FOR YOUR CONVENIENCE!"

Then he'd hear a shout from the other front.

"HEY! YOH! OVER HERE!"

Concluding a sale, he'd move briskly while adding a new bill to his roll.

"COMING! PINE, SCOTCH PINE! TRUCKED IN FROM WILDERNESS!"

"HEY, CHRISTMAS MAN! WHY YA CHARGE MORE FOR THE PINE?!"

"LONGER NEEDLES!" he returned the volley.

And at the conclusion of every sale, the cry of "TIE UP!" A cue for me to run to the scene with rope to tie up the tree for the customer and carry it to their car, wedge it into the trunk and fasten it to the inside hood. If I was lucky there might be a quarter in it for me. But there usually wasn't, as the customer—after haggling with my uncle—was no longer in a festive mood.

But my father seemed to be. There was something about that lot, that square block of dirt, that enlivened him, and he'd often move around it with a holiday air. Away from his grocery store for a month, out from behind the counter which he sometimes called a prison, he became more animated and relaxed.

That wad was getting bigger and bigger. At midday my uncle peeled off half the bills and gave them to my father. By nightfall, over a thousand bucks were in the kitty. Word came that I was to be the bagman. With 1,100 dollars buried in the recesses of my clothing, I stood with my father across from the bus stop on 67th and Kedzie. My orders were clear. When the bus stopped at the light I was to dart across the street, board it, sit in the front, talk to no one, transfer cautiously, get off at Western, run two blocks down a side street, enter the grocery store, nod to my mother at the counter, then speed downstairs to the stockroom and deposit the bag deep inside a designated box of Alpo dog food.

As the years passed, the money runs became more elaborate and my brother would act as a decoy, standing at the bus stop until the last moment. My father signaled me to dart from behind a row of scotch pine, cross the street in traffic and bound onto the bus as my brother disappeared mysteriously behind a drug store.

Who did my father suspect was watching us? My brother joked it was the Nazis. Not the ones from the war, but from the neighborhood—the skinheads who hung out in Marquette Park at the Nazi headquarters of Frank Collins, looking for trouble in all weather.

One morning in the mid-sixties my brother's judgment prevailed. When I arrived at the lot, two squad cars were parked behind the shack. In the middle of the night, skinheads had raided the lot, knocked down the gigantic North Woods sign, demolished Santa's mailbox and painted a swastika on the shack. The idiots also made off with half a dozen balsam and my uncle was steaming. "Probably giving them to their mothers," he said with contempt.

The lot was under a state of alert that night. My brother and I were being sent home early. As I put my gloves to dry on the space heater, I looked out the window of the shack. There in the dark cold dusk of the South Side, I spotted my father between a column of trees, moving apprehensively, as if on guard duty. Was he thinking about the war? How does one find terror on a Christmas tree lot? Put it on the South Side of Chicago.

The shack was sanctuary and storytelling headquarters. When the lot was being whipped with fierce winds and snow, when it was 10 below and the only human braving the elements was my uncle—intent on getting our next buck—I would sit between a space heater and my brother and listen to my father's stories of war and depression.

"You think this is something? Bah, this is nothing. Why, when I was your age, I was at the Yards, salting casings for 24 cents an hour. Outside the gates were 500 jobless, clawing the fence, ready to snatch ours if we dropped or sloughed off."

And then there were the stories of the North Woods before we were born. The year all the trees were sold but one. And my grandfather, a Slovak immigrant who worked as a foreman at the stockyards, was left to settle a dispute between two women haggling over the last tree. Applying the wisdom of Solomon, he grabbed a saw and cut it in half.

"Or take 1950. Hell, that was a year. Your uncle was in Korea, at home there was recession. I had your mother's brother with me. Christmas Eve came and there were boxcars left. Way too many to take to the dump. Naturally we started drinking. That uncle of yours started a fire. Bundle after bundle, crackling wet into the flames. Snow, mud, smoke, fire so intense it was going big as a house."

"What happened, Dad?"

"The firemen came. However, they too had been drinking. I told 'em the hose is not connected but nobody listens. Ashes like a volcano. Pompeii, if you will."

"Sure, why not," I responded with indulgence.

But as I grew older these stories lost their punch, especially those about the lot. Hearing that 1953 was that "bitch year we all got frostbite" did not soften the blizzard of 1966. Still, the stories about the war intrigued me and I wondered why my father kept them so short and sweet.

I longed to prove to him that I had courage and strength, which I felt demonstrated in coping with my libido. Aside from telling a friend, I kept the thing bottled up inside and I felt vaguely suicidal. I wanted to tell my father, as he was a man of the world and might be able to help. But I was too fearful of his reaction.

In the late sixties, when youth rebelled all over the world, my brother chose his moment on the morning we were to unload the last boxcar. He refused to budge from bed. After repeated assurances from my father that he would gladly drag him out of the bed, the tug of war began. Soon both were breathless; it was a draw. Suddenly my father lurched forward, grabbed the end of the mattress, tugged hard and pulled it down the stairs, out the side door and into the snow.

I continued to confine my rebellion to sardonic remarks, feeling bound to my father as a corporal to a sergeant, feeling somewhat honored that as he began to talk more about the war, however vaguely, he did so only in my company. It would take thirty years to hear the whole story, the last story, but even as a teenager I felt a great need to share his unnamed experience.

Sitting in the shack the year before, I had come out to him about my doomed libido. I was still having a rough time deciding which sex I was most attracted to, even after an experience with each that preceding summer. He took the fact that I was attracted to women very well. When I told him of my attraction to men, he blew his stack. He said he'd seen it in the army and did not approve, then asked me why one sex wasn't good enough for me.

After that I went ballistic and nearly began to cry. He got gentler and mentioned England as a place for all types of behavior. I asked if he was suggesting I leave the country. He smiled wearily and said not until the tree season ended. He then suggested I keep busy, bury myself in my work. I turned angry and told him I didn't see things as simplistic as his generation did. Exasperated, he stood up and bellowed: "Decide! One or the other! Men or women! Army or Navy! Scotch pine or balsam!"

Returning to that morning, my father had succeeded in dragging my brother only as far as the driveway, and we had worked without him all day and night unloading the boxcar. Inside the shack my father poured me my first shot of Seagrams VO into a dixie cup. Six months before I had turned eighteen on the same day my father had turned fifty-three. More ironic was that our shared birthday was May 30th, Memorial Day. Dog tired, his bloodshot eyes studied me closely. I had escaped to college that September, and he seemed to be taking the measure of "another college boy." Conversation was difficult between us for another reason. Over Thanksgiving he had caught me stealing condoms from the top shelf of his bedroom closet, a Freudian moment we both longed to forget, his last words to me being: "Put your hands where I can see them."

We drank and he asked me how my homecoming had felt. After being away at school three months, how much had I changed? I responded with teenage wisdom, and he attempted a smile. Then he finished his shot in a gulp, reached for his wallet, or billfold as he called it.

"You know what these are?"

He unfolded two timeworn pages.

"These are discharge papers," he said, placing them on a wooden crate between us, as if these battered pages would now do the talking for him. He had made up his mind to tell me something. And as he sat collecting his thoughts, I sneaked some water into my Seagrams, then belted it down, sensing we were about to march through the jaws of hell.

And then he began. He told me about his homecoming on Christmas Eve in 1945, his problems coping, his inability to stay at the stockyards as they reminded him of the camps. Then we drank more and for some reason I started talking about the Cubs, but he interrupted, which was a relief as he hadn't been listening anyway.

All of the sudden he was talking about the winter of 1944, when the 14th Armored Division was tearing through France and being bombarded day and night by shells from Alsace Alice, a huge artillery cannon mounted on a moving train across the German lines. A week before Christmas half the men in his battalion were blown to bits while sleeping. Then he and other survivors labored all day in the snow collecting their remains, moved out the following morning, fought the next four months, crossed the bridge at Remagen, and entered the sites at Dachau. After a long pause, he got up quickly and moved to the door of the shack.

"That's why you kids are here. I saw so much death in the war, I wanted to bring life into the world."

He opened the door and stood there for a moment.

"That thing you talk about: don't sell yourself short, you'll pull through."

And he stepped out into the snow.

Christmas Eve came. Most years about three hundred trees were left, leaning in pipes, no longer at attention. But there stood my uncle, erect, taking them one by one from the pipes, carrying them to the street and bouncing their trunks on the sidewalk, swatting the snow off the branches with his gloves. And while we worked all day to decamp, he patrolled the sidewalk on Kedzie, shouting to pedestrians, cars, buses, even it seemed to the planes overhead.

"Fresh trees! Select trees! Supply limited!"

Yes, there was still time to get that tree. And for us there was still time to get that buck. Slowly, my father egging us on, my brother and I would rob the rows, quietly taking a tree out of its pipe and dragging it back near the shack to cut it up for the dump.

All day we worked, as the last customers filtered into the lot, most of them expecting, even demanding, a bargain on Christmas Eve. But they never bargained for my uncle, or with him. Most were broken by that stone face and tireless refusal to come down more than a quarter. But not all, for this was the old neighborhood, the very soil on which my uncle had learned his techniques. And so, South Sider to South Sider, iron butt to iron butt, they went at it, haggling till sundown, as my father and brother and I took down the shack, dug up the pipe and hauled them away, filled in the holes, and cut up the trees for the dump. One of us chopped while the other hurled the branches into the trailer. My father collected the skeletons from the tallest trees and, using them as posts, wedged them in along the sides of the open U-Haul, giving us room to pile branches as high as the posts would reach.

At 9 o'clock we were still running and robbing the rows. Now the lot looked like a plundered battlefield. Nothing left to do but bury the dead. Yet my uncle was dragging them from the alley and putting them back in the pipes, claiming there would be customers if we waited just a while longer. An argument erupted between the two brothers, a truce arranged, settlement arrived at. We could take the trees from the last ten rows. We would wait one hour before condemning the trees at the Front.

The cold sky cleared, the moon came out and still we hadn't left for the dump. There was always one more thing to do. Always a few pipes that wouldn't budge from the frozen ground, that would lose us another hour. Aching for the warmth of home, eager to begin Christmas, I looked at the clock inside the insurance building across the street and measured the time left to get to a party or join a buddy in a bar, and quickly felt all plans disintegrate. My father approached as I dug the shovel deep into the ground around the pipe.

"What's wrong? Did it conquer ya?"

"Can't we just leave this one? For Christ's sake, Dad, it's almost eleven," I said.

"You don't want to come out here Christmas Day, do ya? Alright then."

All three of us on one pipe, heaving, pounding with shovels and picks to the limit of our endurance. Finally, word came that we would decamp and head for the dump.

That year, when I was eighteen and had heard the Story of the War, my brother and I filled the trailer too high. Afraid that the load would shift when he turned or hit a bump, my father ordered us to climb on top of the U-Haul, where we spread our weight over the branches. The trailer jolted as the station wagon spun its wheels in the snow, then moved forward and turned the corner past the gas station.

Soon we were travelling up the hill over the Nabisco factory, the winter air sweetened with the smell of cookies. Laying on a bed of balsam, looking up at the stars in a cold December sky, all around us was the dark enormous city. Up the hill we went, over the factories and plants, the cold, bleak, Dickensian, industrial South, on our way on Christmas Eve... to the dump.

On top of the hill, one could see as far as the Southeast, the inferno of mills billowing smoke and hundreds of fires in the night. All at once I saw the South Side: an ancient battlefield. And I felt its spilled blood inside me, blood that had tugged at me since birth. Blood from the stockyards, blood from the steel mills, blood from the wars. Looking up at the stars, moving up the hill, surrounded by the city, I felt lifted by the end of another season, and a new connection with my father.

I saw us toiling on that lot together with our private battles. I saw my father living with war's memories of darkness and devastation, but somehow forging from them an awareness of particular values—what you live for. My father using his story to help his son in his lesser war. My father keeping a flame alive, holding back the darkness, living in the light.

And so, at last, up there on that bed of balsam, I gave in to it and admitted that part of me loved this region, even that sad lot on Kedzie. At that moment I no longer felt enlisted in somebody else's war, but in my own. Above, the stars appeared to merge into a single light, time and space ceased to matter. Suddenly I experienced what my father seemed to be searching for on that lot, searching for since that day he returned from war on Christmas Eve twenty-three years before. Transcendence.

As so often happens, our epiphanies are interrupted by banalities. It was my job to watch out for cops up there. As always, it was the taillight on the trailer, that goddamn wire disconnecting as the U-Haul swung and turned. Coming out of my reverie, I heard a cop calling us to climb down. As I descended with my brother, I saw my father taking out his billfold. Instead of presenting his license, he took out his discharge papers and handed them to the cop. I looked at the cop as he unfolded those pages from the past. My eyes darted back to my father. There was a dumbstruck silence. Then both men erupted in laughter, the laughter of communion between soldier and cop. We were let off the hook and sent on our way.

Home near midnight, to the house over the family grocery store, where my mother and sisters had held down the fort all month. Where they spent the last few hours wrapping presents after the store closed. My mother greeted us at the side door with tired affection.

"Hey fellas, you're here. Finally. I bet you're beat," she said.

And then, with an apologetic smile, she added, "First, go downstairs. Go right down and change those clothes. I don't want those needles in my house."

Down to the basement we'd clomp. The warmth of the furnace, the smell of our late dinner cooking, and slowly the infection of bad humor, the feeling of being winter's plowboy, was replaced with a kind of contentment. Christmas had been won, the war had ended, and the troops were home.

41

Three Lunatic Misunderstandings of the Urban Midwest *Eileen Favorite*

"And here occurred one of those wild,
almost lunatic misunderstandings which are
part of the daily experiences of childhood."
—George Orwell

1. I grew up 13 miles from Gary, Indiana, and I thought that if I danced well enough in front of my living room window, the Jacksons might drive by my house and see my mad moves and ask me to join the band.

2. I believed that the news anchor for WLS Channel 7 news, ABC, Fahey Flynn, was the mayor of Chicago, Richard J. Daley. Both men had jowly, Irish faces. Both men were balding with white hair wisping over their pates. Both men wore suits, but Fahey preferred bowties, which I considered an easy costume change. And it worried me, I thought it might be a little unfair, for the mayor to be part of the Eyewitness News Team. I didn't say anything to anyone. I just watched and I worried. Fahey rhymed with Daley too. *Fahey Daley.* By 1976, when Fahey Flynn reported that the mayor had died suddenly from a heart attack, I had long figured out that they were

42

two different men. But I have to say, from then on, as his hair and skin grew ever whiter, Fahey Flynn always looked like a ghost to me, as if he might be reporting the news from the beyond.

3. I wanted to live in the Robert Taylor Homes. We'd drive down the Dan Ryan, on the way to Grandma's apartment, and I'd think how cool it would be to live in a big apartment building with your friends on the same floor. How great it would be if you didn't have to cross the lawn or street to go visit them, if you didn't have to hop a fence or push through the fir trees to get to your friend's house. Instead, you could just walk across the hall and knock on a door and there would be Marguerite. There would be Kitty. You wouldn't need boots or umbrellas because your friend lived right in the same building.

Vargas *Joseph G. Peterson*

Because he works as a nighttime janitor in a large bank in the Loop, he has access to things. He says: You have no idea what I have access to. The art alone in these places is unbelievable. Much of it should be in a museum.

You don't really know him, but he likes to sit down next to you when he comes to the Bar. Why does he pick you to sit next to, of all people? As far as you can tell, you and he have nothing in common.

He's told you the following facts many, *many* times: He is Croatian. He fishes coho salmon and brown trout off the shore of Lake Michigan with a trout line that he shoots out into the far distance with a fire extinguisher that makes a *pop* when he shoots the line out there and a claw hook that holds the line deep on the bottom of the lake so all the vertical hooks can descend into the water, already baited. Once the rig is set, he drinks Slivovitz waiting for the coho. When he's not fishing his trout line, he's on the Des Plaines River fishing carp.

He says: When I catch the carp, I like to keep them alive for a few days and let them swim in my bathtub that I fill with milk. That way I let the fish clear out all the mud from their mud veins and they will be that much more sweet when I eat them.

You've never fished in your life. You've never eaten carp soaked in milk.

One day he shows up to the Bar with a present for you. It's a Vargas pin-up.

He says: Do you know what this is?

He opens very carefully a bag with the picture of a naked woman who has yellow hair. Her legs are chastely crossed at the knees. You have some idea what it is, but you're not willing to say.

Why is he showing this to you? Why is he coming so close? Doesn't

44

he see that you and he have nothing in common?

He likes vodka.

You like tequila.

There's really no place in the middle where the two of you might meet. Yet he keeps trying. He says: You want to join me while I shoot out my trout line? I will bring the Slivovitz and we will toast happy times.

You don't believe in happy times. You only believe in the very specific problems brought on by drinking: of how to pay for the next one, and of how to pay for the next one after that, and so on. Also, there is always the question of how to arrive and depart this godforsaken dump on your own terms. And how to make it home alive and in one piece, which is not so easy. The sidewalks are broken. The key to your apartment doesn't work very well. The other night you couldn't get in, and so you slept curled up underneath a bush in the courtyard. It's okay. You were tired enough, so you slept, even while the local raccoons went about their nocturnal business.

Anyway, these were the practicalities you were thinking about when he showed you the picture, and then you promptly forgot these practicalities making it more likely you would think them again after you are done talking to him.

As you stare at the Vargas pin-up, the Croatian janitor quickly puts it back in the bag. He says: I can't be seen carrying this picture. It is a Vargas pin-up. Do you know what that means? Do you?

No, you tell him, I don't know what that means.

He says: It means, I will sell it to you for only two hundred and fifty dollars, but I make that offer to you only because you are my friend.

With that he orders another round of drinks, and while you think on the meaning of that price for that possibly stolen picture, he raises his glass. He says: To the old happy times!

It's puzzling that he should put it this way because you've never spent a single happy time with him, or practically with anyone else for that matter. You don't really know what a happy time is. You know what Happy Hour is but not happy time. Nevertheless, you raise your glass. What other choice do you have? The rules dictate it and so you say with him, touching his glass with yours, your pinky finger extended: *Prost*. Cheers. *Nostrovia!*

In your mind, however, you are a chained tiger leaping against the bars of the cage.

On the Way   *Cyn Vargas*

People used to say I was my daddy's girl. I went everywhere with him, to the store, to the mechanic, to his poker games because he said I was his good luck charm. He and Mom would laugh when they weren't fighting. Things never seemed that bad, and when Dad left for work one day and didn't come home, I didn't know why.

"He's just gone, baby," Mom said. Soon after that, she began working double shifts, and Grandma— Dad's mom—moved in with us a little after that. She'd been kicked out of her nursing home for cursing out the staff and throwing things at the other patients. Again.

Mom wouldn't tell me where Dad went, and after a few weeks I stopped asking. But I wrote him letters that I crammed into blank envelopes and put in the mailbox down the street. I never told anyone about this, not even my best friend, Benny. I knew they would never get to Dad, but they had to go somewhere, I figured.

Grandma yanked me by the arm while waiting for the Cicero bus; her sharp nails dug into my skin. The bus doors opened and she pulled me up the steps as though afraid I'd escape.

"She nine," Grandma yelled at the bus driver, a fat woman with CTA stretched out beyond recognition on her wide blue sleeve. The bus driver bent at the waist as far as she could. One of her hairy brows raised, and she eyed me up and down like I was a criminal.

"You're nine?" she asked me. I felt Grandma's nails on the back of my neck, and I nodded.

"She nine," Grandma said again. Sighs and a couple of c'mons

46

echoed from the back. I hadn't been nine for almost five years.

The bus driver waved her big hand, and we boarded. There were two empty seats left—one way in the back where some kids sat and laughed, and one toward the front where the old people were. Grandma said nothing and shoved me into the seat between two old folks that reeked of Bengay and hairspray.

"You're not nine," said one of the old ladies. Her hands were shaking, and the bunch of keys that hung off the strap of her purse jangled. Her lips were thin and wrinkled, just like the rest of her. She had big brown blotches on her face, the color of the oatmeal cookies we ate at home.

"Yeah, you're not nine," said the other. Her lips had no wrinkles, but her hands had big blue veins, like pipes beneath her skin.

I did what I usually do when I don't know what to say to strangers. I acted like I didn't understand.

I shook my head and raised my arms, my palms toward the sky like I was balancing an invisible glass in each one. It was easier than explaining Grandma didn't want to dish out an extra buck to let me on the bus even though she had wads of cash in her bra. I had watched her take out a stack of bills, damp with sweat and smelling like the Walgreen's perfume she wore, to pay for things like vitamins and pantyhose at stores.

The old lady with permed hair shook her head. She sneered at me and said, "You're a liar. You should be ashamed of yourself."

Her words made my skin itch. I looked to my side and the other old lady was nodding in agreement. I leaned even further to scan the back of the bus, past the couple making out, and the baby crying and flailing its arms like it was winding up to fly away, and spotted Grandma eating one of her cookies that she always kept inside her purse, wrapped in like twenty napkins. I wanted to get up, walk over, and yank that cookie out of her mouth. She'd put me in that seat. She'd refused to pay because she was cheap. She dragged me everywhere since Mom had to go to work. And she was the one that made sure I knew that my dad left almost half a year ago because Mom and I didn't make him happy. I stared at Grandma and wished she could feel my eyes on her.

In the mornings, she'd stomp from our spare room and plop down at the breakfast table. It was my responsibility to make sure we ate, since Mom had to leave for work before the sun came up. Grandma would shoot herself up with the medicine for her diabetes and wait at the table 'til I was finished cooking breakfast: eggs, no salt, toast, no butter, hand-squeezed orange juice from the oranges she got from the guy that sold fruit out of the back of his truck.

We got mangos from the fruit truck guy, too. I loved mangos. I loved slicing them up in three perfect pieces and sprinkling them with chili powder and lemon juice and sucking the juice from them. Dad taught me how to eat mangos like that. We'd sit on the back porch and he would scrunch up his face and smile, "This chili is hot. Too hot for you, Lucia." I would take him up on his challenge. I'd take a piece of mango off his plate, the fruit slimy under my fingertips, raise it to my lips, the juices dripping onto my lap, and take a bite. I'd try not to make a face, but he would watch me and laugh when my eyes began watering.

I was staring at the floor of the bus when I saw Grandma's familiar shoes.

"Vamanos," she said, and hurled me off my seat. I turned back to the two old ladies, but neither of them bothered to look at me.

She wouldn't let go of my wrist as we walked. This meant she was tired, and with her swollen ankles, couldn't walk as fast as I could. She used me to keep her balance.

In these moments, moments when she needed me—like when she couldn't get the needle in or needed me to make her breakfast—she didn't say one word about Mom. Didn't call her bad words in Spanish and say she was the reason my father left because "a real wife stayed home and didn't go out to work," the reason I was a spoiled brat, the reason she was going to die without seeing her son again. Mom told me Grandma was just old and bitter and to ignore her, but all I wanted to do was yell at her. I think Mom hoped that Dad would come back one day and see how great she was for taking care of his mother.

"Alli," she said pointing to some dirty, stone building that looked abandoned.

"What is this place?" I said, but Grandma, who understood more English than she let on, just slapped me on the back and pushed me toward the door.

The lobby smelled musty. A dusty gumball machine with no gumballs sat in the corner. Almost all the seats in the room were filled with women; the only males were babies, cradled in their mothers' laps. One little boy with barely any hair played all alone near a chair with a teensy paper cup.

Grandma approached the counter and said she had an appointment. Behind it a woman took down her name. They spoke in Spanish. I didn't let Grandma know that I knew more Spanish than I let on. The lady told us to take a seat. We sat together next to a woman who anxiously tapped her feet, like she was sending Morse code. From a bottle with a picture of a strawberry on it, she rubbed pink lotion into the folds of fat in her arms. The too-sweet smell of it filled the lobby.

"Fabian!" a nurse yelled from an open door by the counter just a few minutes later.

We both stood. Grandma pushed me on the back of my head to move me forward.

The nurse showed us to a room at the end of a narrow hallway. A man with a white coat stood there holding a clipboard. He smirked at me, and I immediately didn't like him.

"Hola, Doña Miriam," he said, and they kissed on the cheek like they were old friends.

"Is this little Lucia?" he said in English.

"Humph. Not so little," Grandma said in Spanish.

She grabbed my stomach and pinched it. I winced. "She's eats like a boy. She eats everything."

"We can take care of that," the man said, and then looked at me. He turned and picked up a syringe off the table. "You should lose twenty pounds. How old are you, Lucia?"

"Almost fourteen," I said. I stared at the syringe. "See? Now is the time. You'll want a boyfriend soon. Now, lower your pants. I need to give this shot in your behind."

"Ahorita," Grandma said.

"No." I stepped back.

"Lucia, don't be scared. It's just a shot, a secret formula that will make you beautiful. I'll give you pills, too."

He got closer and I could see the brown liquid in the syringe. I shook my head.

Grandma slapped me hard. I kept my face still, refusing to show it hurt even as the pain shot into my cheekbone and stayed there. The doctor stayed silent.

"Ahorita," Grandma repeated, and I unbuttoned my pants and pulled them down. The needle felt as thick as a tree as it slid beneath my skin and then slowly came back out. I wanted to cry, but held it in.

"Good. Now, maybe I can finally say you're my granddaughter."

I walked into the lobby and surveyed the room. I guess all the women were there for the same reason. They all wanted shots and pills. They all wanted to be pretty. The pain from the shot spread to my chest as we walked out of the building and into the bright sun. Grandma smiled at me for the first time in a while, as though whatever had been in that shot was transforming me already.

The next morning, Mom was still working her double shift, so I didn't have a chance to tell her. Grandma called me from the kitchen.

"Yes, Grandma," I said. I trudged over to the fridge and took out the eggs and the cheese and the oranges. She sat at the table rubbing alcohol on a cotton ball over the same spot on her thigh, blue veins thin as strands of hair under her skin.

"It's almost six months since your dad left. You know why, don't you?"

The eggs slowly began to cook. I carelessly turned them over in the warming pan. I didn't like to see her inject herself. She always made it a point to make a face that showed how much it pained her.

After she was done, she rubbed the injection with the same cotton ball and said, "He left because you're fat, Lucia. Who wants a fat daughter?" She drank her orange juice. A little spilled from the corner of her mouth. She tapped her plate, and I pushed the eggs, brown with cheese, from the skillet. She picked up her fork and stuck me in the side. "I'd be embarrassed, too. Did you take those pills the doctor gave you?"

I sat down next to her. A bit of egg stuck to the mole near her mouth. I nodded, but we both knew I was lying. She hit my hand with her fork, and I got up and went to my room. I heard her humming as I grabbed the pill bottle that the doctor gave us the day before.

When I came back to the kitchen, there was a glass of water in front of my seat. I opened the bottle and threw a pill into my mouth. It wasn't coated, and the sour taste almost made me gag. I took a big gulp of the water and swallowed.

"Now, remember. Don't tell your mother about this. I'm just trying to help. When your dad comes back for me, maybe he'll stay this time. If you and your mother can get it together." She ate the last of her eggs. I waited 'til she was done to wash the dishes, and when I heard her snore from her late afternoon nap, I snuck out of the house in hopes of finding Benny.

Benny used to look up to my dad. He lived down the block in a house with a yard where the bushes were groomed to look like different animals: a dinosaur, a llama, and a spider, even. His dad and mine had been friends long before we were born. Benny's mom had left years ago, so now it was just him and his dad.

Benny and I liked to go to the park down the street. We'd talk about movies or school, or sometimes we'd talk about his mom and where she could have gone. Sometimes we'd talk about my dad and why he left. We could only wonder, because no one ever told us anything.

I found Benny in the park playing basketball by himself. He waved at me and jogged over. My stomach got a nervous feeling, probably from the pill I'd taken. I wanted to tell him what my grandma was making me do. As we started walking, he slung his arm around my shoulder, holding the basketball in the other. Benny said, "Walking with you must be what it's like to get hip checked in the NHL." He laughed and pushed me playfully.

There was no one in the park. Benny was wearing the track jacket that used to be his dad's. The wind blew my hair around and some strands stuck to my lips. Some birds called to one another between the trees and the sun came out, making our shadows darker. I watched mine, falling on the pathway bordered by dying grass, swaying left to right as I walked. My hips nearly took up the whole sidewalk.

"Benny likes you," Julia had told me one day in class. "He's gonna try to kiss you soon, and probably feel you up." We giggled. I hoped now that he'd grab me and kiss me. I'd even let him feel me up, even though I didn't really have any boobs. Benny's shadow came closer to mine, both of them stretched out on the cement like people bigger than us. I looked up at him. Benny's pimples were all in one cluster on his forehead, but everywhere else his skin was smooth. He smiled at me. He had those clear braces that you could still see.

"You mad?" he said.

"Nope," I said, and he put his arm around me again. Our shadows were one for a moment.

"Seriously, hip check!" He laughed again and we stopped underneath a tree. We were almost in high school, and we would be going to different ones. I knew that soon things would change for us. New schools. New friends. New girls around him. Who knew if we would still hang out as much.

Nothing ever stayed the same for long. Mom and Dad proved that. I wanted to tell him how Grandma called me fat, how Mom was always working, how I'd been crying in my room a lot lately. I wanted to tell him this, but I didn't want to lose him, too. I didn't want to drive him away like Dad, so instead I didn't say a word.

Underneath that tree, Benny turned his head one way, then the other, and finally kissed me. I heard the basketball fall to the ground, his hands on my hips. We opened our mouths, our tongues touched, and his soft lips met mine.

"I better get back before my grandma wakes up," I said when it was over, and he smiled.

"Yeah. She's crazy."

When we got to my house, we stopped out front and we smiled again. "Let's meet up tomorrow," Benny said.

"OK."

When I walked inside my house, Dad was sitting on the couch. Grandma sat next to him. He was wearing the shirt that I had given him a few months back for Father's Day, right before he left. It was so white against his dark arms. His hair was longer than it had been when he'd left, and wavier than I remembered. His glasses were perched mid-nose like always, and he pushed them up when he saw me. His eyes were wide, the amber speckles in them twinkling like they used to do when he'd tell me he loved me. He stepped forward, his arms rising up slowly like strings were lifting them. I noticed he wasn't wearing his wedding ring.

"Lucia," he said. Grandma held tight to his hand, not letting it go. "I'm sorry I left the way I did. It's just—"

I didn't let him finish. I ran out of the house and called after Benny, who waited for me to catch up. I pretended not to hear Dad shouting my name.

Benny waved at him. "Hey, your dad is back!" he said, and started to walk back toward my house.

"No!" I took his hand. "Please, Benny." I didn't need to say anymore. He knew from my eyes, my voice, in the way I touched his wrist that I had to go. He held onto my hand, and we walked together toward his house.

"Why don't you want to see your dad? I thought you'd be happy," Benny said. We sat on his couch. The house was quiet, his father out.

"I don't want to talk about it," I said, but I did. I wanted to tell Benny everything.

Instead of words, I began to cry, and he put his arm around me again.

"C'mon," he said after a minute. He stood up and grabbed my hand. "You need to go talk to your dad."

"No."

"Lucia, if it were my mom who came back, I would talk to her. You're lucky."

"Fine," I said.

He walked me back to my house. "I have to be back before my dad gets home, but call me or come over later, OK?"

I nodded.

When I wandered into my house, Grandma was still on the couch. Dad next to her. He looked up from his hands when he heard me come in.

"Lucia. Please, let me explain," he said. I followed him into the kitchen. We stood on opposite sides of the table. The sun was setting and all I could see was Dad cloaked in a soft glow.

"I don't expect you to understand. Your mom and I, we just fought so much."

"So, you left? You fought with Mom, and you left without saying anything?"

I started crying but didn't bother wiping the tears away. I clenched my fists at my sides so tight, my knuckles hurt.

"I know you're mad. I'm sorry. I shouldn't have done that. I love you. I just had to go, and then time just went so fast." He pulled out a chair and sat down. His put his elbows on the table and held his head in his hands.

"Did you leave us for another family? Is that it?" I shouted.

Tears began to roll down his cheeks. The glow was fading.

"No. It's nothing like that. I'm sorry. I should have told you. I should have come sooner." He went to say more but cried into his palms instead.

"Does Mom know you're here?"

He nodded. I crossed my arms, feeling my heart ram into my chest.

"I got my own place not too far away from here. I'm taking Grandma to live with me. She and your mom never got along anyway. Do you want to come see it? Your mom said it's up to you." He wanted me to say yes. I wanted to say yes, too.

"No."

"Lucia, I didn't leave because of you," Dad said as I walked out of the kitchen, not turning back.

I hid under the covers until the house was quiet. I left my room, only hearing my footsteps. I threw the diet pills down the kitchen sink and washed them away. I pushed the chair Dad had sat in back underneath the table. I stepped out onto the back porch. On the step was a plate of mango, cut up in three perfect pieces. A small black bug crawled across the plate. I kicked it away. I wiped my eyes and looked up at the sky. There was no moon, no stars. I waited for Mom to come home.

The Harpy *Nancy Werking Poling*

There's plenty to go around but we fight over scraps. In the alley, less than a block from the library where Laura works. Our raspy calls compete with the squeaking brakes of delivery trucks. Not far from where my sister catalogs and shelves, then shelves and catalogs. In my claws I grasp the remains of a McDonald's cinnamon roll. What call number would it have, Laura, you who must organize everything? Or should I ask what caw number? As I cackle over my sense of humor, my beak opens, and I accidentally drop the piece of cinnamon roll. Another crow strutting down the alley, bobbing his head forward then back, forward then back, observes my mistake and scurries toward my morsel. I could fight for it, I guess, but decide not to.

I refuse to eat indoors.

"For God's sake, Lark," Laura whispers, "can't you sit like a woman instead of—instead of—you're the only person I know who squats on a chair."

I try, I've always tried to do what she says. I concentrate on my left leg, pulling it out from beneath my haunches, straightening it, slowly, deliberately, until it sticks straight out in front of me. Now my right leg supports my weight. Flapping my arms, I lift my torso, up, up, ever so slightly.

The green plastic chair tilts to the right, balances for a moment on two legs, then spills me onto the sidewalk, where I lie staring up at the sky. "For everyone to see," Laura hisses. I don't care that people have turned their heads in my direction. I do care that a black Labrador—at first, I see little more than his giant head staring into my face—has placed his front paws on my chest and is barking a signal that the chase is on. Can't he see I'm in no shape to engage in a contest? His owner, a middle-aged man in shorts and a

55

soaked gray t-shirt, tries not to break the rhythm of his jog, bouncing up and down in place while the dog refuses to let me get up. A harsh jerk of the chain and a few words of profanity draw Fido to his owner's side. I arch my back and turn my head to see the runner still bouncing up and down, this time while he waits for the light to change so he can cross the street. The Lab looks back at me with longing.

"Is she all right?" people ask my sister.

You wouldn't see her collecting books from the bin and not checking carefully when each is due, yet Laura assures everyone that I'm fine.

I'm still lying on the sidewalk, still eyeing the Lab and its owner (who now run down Sheridan Road) when I spot within arm's reach the blueberry scone I was holding when I fell. I reach for it and take a bite. Laura whispers a reprimand. She's an expert whisperer, Laura is, because of her job I suppose. I yell at her that I'm a dainty dumpster eater. She doesn't laugh, just whispers, "That's been on the sidewalk where dogs walk, as one just did, and—and you don't know what germs are there."

She throws the scone into the trash can and goes inside the cafe to buy me another. I lift myself from the sidewalk, hop over to the trash can, and take out my scone.

For the next—how long is it in bird years?—for a God-awful long time I try to behave like a human being, nodding my head at everything she says. Yet I must stay alert, not let her dull voice lure me into carelessness. My head jerks from right to left, left to right. My piercing eyes take in the actions of everyone around me. Customers at other green plastic tables read their Sunday *Tribune*s, sip their lattes. Muffins and bagels atop white paper doilies tempt me. Laura would buy me more, but the pleasure's not in the eating as much as in the snatching.

People walk in every direction, some through the aisle between tables, some crossing at the light, some defying drivers who have the green light. Many carry lawn chairs toward the lake. I'm anxious to get there myself. Meanwhile, Laura talks about her job at the library, how she caught somebody book-snatching the other day and chased him all the way to the Cinemax. I picture Laura running after the book-snatcher, and I'm cheering for him. She wouldn't understand that he was trying to rescue the spirit trapped in the book, the spirit trying to fly up, up until no one can cram it back onto a shelf.

Laura, the guard who keeps spirits captive. That's why the library is brick, it's easier to keep the spirits inside.

I peer into her face, trying to see the essence of one who is a guard of spirits. Her face—it looks like mine: long crooked nose, wide forehead, except she covers hers with bangs. Her hands, too, are like mine, with long fingers. She, though, clips her fingernails into slivered moons. Given her job of sorting and shelving she doesn't dare let them grow into the talons mine are, she's told me. In my line I don't dare keep mine short, I've told her. And what exactly is your line, she often whispers. She doesn't think I do anything, and she wants me to admit it.

I want to fly away, escape this woman who catalogs my mind, deciding where I should be shelved. Trying to trap my spirit.

When she's finished her cappuccino and swallowed the last bite of cranberry muffin she says it's time to take me back. Okay by me. As usual, she stands outside the door of my room, and instead of saying I hope you had a good time or it's been great being with you, she lectures me. I stay ahead of her, having memorized the list. "For health reasons," I chirp before she says, "If for no other reason, you must take a bath for health reasons."

"And social reasons," I chirp as she begins to explain that nobody wants to be around a woman whose body odor precedes her.

"You need to bathe for social reasons," she says. "You know why that dog was sniffing you, don't you?" Before I have a chance to answer that some dogs have been bred to track birds, she says, "Because of your odor. Really, dear,"—she always says dear when she's lecturing me—"I can hardly stand the stench myself."

I don't defend myself, not anymore. I don't remind her that she's the one who spent two weeks in bed last spring, and that even though I have these habits that supposedly make me more prone to disease, I haven't been sick in years. I don't remind her that I have many feathered friends.

At last, she's gone, and I'm free to fly away.

We're a watchful group, the ten of us perched on the rusty wall extending into the lake. The wind ruffles my soft white feathers, creating a natural air-conditioning. As if a gun has been shot, we rise as one, our back and forth calls shrill and joyful. I play with the wind, letting it lift me higher, higher yet, until I change direction and dive toward the water, then effortlessly swoop upward again.

Laura could never imagine this, the freedom of being uncatalogued. Laura who sits at a desk all day and whispers answers to people's questions and organizes books—910.23, then 910. 24, then 910.25. Mustn't let them get mixed up, the books. Must keep order. It's a lovely building, she often tells me. A great height to crap from, I've said. That's disgusting, she's told me more than once.

Back on the wall we watch young children tiptoe into the water then rush out, shrieking in delight. I bring to the other gulls' attention that a woman has fallen asleep on a beach towel and her skin is turning the deep pink of an evening western sky. We try to warn her, swooping down, calling loudly back and forth. "Goddamn you birds!" she yells up at us, obviously not appreciating our kindness. She walks to the water's edge to rinse off her leg as we all laugh.

At the picnic I grab the biggest piece of food, press my claws against the table, and lift off. It isn't greed that motivates me but the delight of taking from humans the things they hold on to. The same may be said of the way they cling tightly to the spirit. It is only free when it has been wrested from those who try to control it.

The evening is too humid, my room too confining. I head for the El overpass, where my fellow pigeons roost. Now my body is leaden in color, heavy and clumsy. The calls I make to my neighbors are not shrill, not raspy, but soft and low and soothing.

It's late. I flap my wings and lift my body up to the metal girder. There's a lot of movement: rustling feathers, shifting positions, accusations that somebody's taking up too much space. The sounds, even when there's disagreement, are soft and soothing. Not people noises that put my nerves on edge and make me think only of escape.

Before I've had time to tuck in my wings, I notice the body. Back where the glow of the streetlight doesn't reach, where a passerby won't trip over it. Have any of you noticed? I ask around. I can tell the others don't want to see, don't want to know. I drop down and stand on the concrete, inches from his face.

The eyes are closed. There is no movement, no even breathing of the drunk or the sleeping. I hop around, checking for a sign of life. There is none. I'm overcome with worry about his soul. It must not get into the wrong hands. Not into the hands of librarians like Laura, who will catalog it and shelve it in a place where it will be forgotten.

I think of the boulders down at the lake, the crevasses between them where water rushes in, swirls, then moves back out into the depths.

I will not let your soul get into the hands of the librarians, I promise. I will lift it, carry it up, up, over to the lake. Then I will carefully hide it among the rocks, in a place the water rushes into, so that you will be carried out. Out into the peaceful depths of the dark blue water. You will be free.

I put my soft feathers against his face.

My Generation   *Ines Bellina*

It's taken years but I've finally perfected an answer to a question that makes me feel awkward, a tad embarrassed, and uncharacteristically shy. It's a question I get asked less and less often, but one that inevitably pops up whenever someone learns of my globetrotting ways or asks about my life pre-Chicago. The question: "What was it like living in New York?" My answer: "I didn't really have a typical New York experience so I'm probably not the right person to talk about it."

Of course, this will prompt more questions that make me talk about it, and maybe I am the right person to talk about doing New York wrong. Because think of what the city has done to our collective imagination. New York is where Rachel flees when she leaves her groom stranded at the altar. New York is where Dan Humphrey goes from creepy high school lurker to the kind of man who has a threesome with Hillary Duff. It's where Carrie can afford to live in a Greenwich Village apartment thanks to one measly column, where Charlotte has a painting of her vagina, where Miranda is immortalized in a Broadway play, and where Samantha Jones is transformed into a beacon of hope. New York is where Felicity Porter cuts her hair and unleashes a national debate. It's where Hannah Horvath says nothing of interest and manages to become a voice of a generation.

This was not my New York, though when I packed my bags for grad school, I did think it would eventually become that. To a certain extent, I was the archetype that so populates the genre of shows about 20-something life set in the city: a fresh-faced horny young woman with writerly pursuits and an overwhelming desire to have the world at her fingertips. What I got instead was a lot of stability. If most people see their 20s as a series of cringe-worthy mistakes, I see it as one of the few times in my life where I had my shit together. I was in a fully funded grad program that shielded me from not only the crappy jobs of youth but from the 2008 recession. I had a steady boyfriend that never wavered on his devotion to me. I had a built-in friend group from my undergrad. I had so much work and reading that most of my memories of the place are trapped somewhere in Columbia's Butler Library instead of the boroughs.

When I moved to Chicago, married and ready to get out in the job market, I felt like I had either made the genius move of protecting myself from the heartaches of my twenties or the terrible mistake of wrapping myself up in a cocoon of safety. Nothing about my experience in New York reflected the grittiness and personal transformation the TV shows so convincingly promised. I felt very much the same as when I had arrived, but with a lot more French theory in my brain.

Chicago was supposed to be my adult world, where I would do adult things like be married, have babies, dabble in real estate and enjoy extremely low-key dinners with other couples where we would talk about mortgages and neighborhood associations and succulents. Soon after moving, my marriage went downhill, my career went nowhere, and the only friend I made moved away. Before I knew it, I found myself divorced, single, in a dead-end job, with only the most tepid of social connections.

Thus began the so-called coming-of-age generation defining chapter of my life that would make for an excellent TV show. Except I was in my 30s and the city was Chicago. The tropes were different from those in *Girls, Living Single, Sex and the City, How I Met Your Mother* et al. And they weren't what you see in Chicago shows like *E.R, Chicago Fire, Chicago PD, Chicago Janitors,* or whatever else Dick Wolf has up his sleeve. In my experience, the intrepid protagonist in a coming-of-age TV show set in Chicago would experience the following tropes:

- The shitty, underpaid job of our protagonist will not be in a sexy industry like media, fashion or finance. It will be in an ad agency that is desperately trying to function like a start-up because they too feel out-of-touch.
- Our hero will still be trying to make it as a writer but is fully aware that she will need a day job for the rest of eternity because the Midwest is nothing if not great at keeping your feet on the ground.
- There will be an improv season, a podcast season, and a stand-up season, which will include the same recurrent guest stars because the

Venn diagram of people who are interested in all three is one perfect overlapping circle.

- There won't be any roommate hijinks because our fearless character can afford rent on her own. There will be, however, amusing landlord drama like the one time her nonagenarian building admin demanded she go without flushing the toilet for a few days after her pipes freeze during a polar vortex. "Like in Old Country."

- There will be at least one bottle episode set during a polar vortex. Fine, there will be several.

- Every season, an animal will unite the city, and she will be an active and enthusiastic participant in this, the most Star-Hollowesque of traditions.

- There won't be a montage of dates gone awry, a la *Master of None*, just a long sequence of Tinder messages saying "hey" with the occasional "uh, looks like I came down with something" mixed in.

- There will be men, of course. No Mr. Big, but definitely an insecure image-obsessed jerk who strings her along.

- There won't be an Aiden, but there will be a plethora of white men in flannel trying to convince her of the beauty of #cabinlife.

- She will stop dalliances with not one but TWO members of the Democratic Socialists of America.

- The climax of her romantic crises will have Pitchfork as a background, always Pitchfork.

- Three men will tell her they love her. One because he is used to it, another one because he means it, and one who takes it back.

- There will be a particularly heartbreaking yet hilarious scene when she sobs out of sadness while getting a tattoo from a man named Bunny, who is himself dealing with the fallout of a decade-long relationship.

- She will have guy friends, actual guy friends. None will be secretly in love with her. There will be no wacky one-night stands with them. She will not pine in silence for any. They will mostly be there to provide drunken nights, where the only conversations will consist of retelling other drunken nights because no one, not even her, wants to talk or think about feelings. The escapades will end at The Owl before she spends hours wandering the streets in search of the Tamale Guy.

- She will form friendships with women too, and those who use "they" pronouns, and she'll realize the only people who could sustain an all-white cast in their own show are those who live in Lincoln Park for a few years before moving to Dubuque, Iowa to pop out babies.

- Most of these friendships will be genuine, sincere, and loving. Sometimes there will be a falling out, but it usually won't go beyond a strained once-a-year run in, where all parties will avoid talking about said falling out because people here are polite and can really push down their discomfort for the sake of everyone else.

- Our antihero won't be able to keep up with her friends' long-distance bike riding group, so she'll start drifting away from them, too.

- She'll lose friends to marriage, children, the suburbs, but mostly she'll lose friends to LA. This she has in common with her NY counterparts.

- Talking about NY, there will be crossover episodes featuring her East Coast friends. Most will be cool. All will lose their minds at the cost of rentals. A few will be a little too shocked that Chicago bars can also be worthy of Instagram hashtags. One in particular will really, really push for the Midwest equals Red State trap, insisting that everyone she keeps meeting is a conservative even though she has yet to leave the four-block radius near Navy Pier. Our hero will retort, "Chicago gave us Obama, New York gave us Trump" and that specific scene will be in the reel sent to the Emmys' committee.

- There will one season finale that involves the federal indictment of someone she knows because this is Chicago after all.

- At some point, our protagonist will look around and feel tired. Her old haunts will be populated with those younger and hipper than her. What's even more telling is she won't care that they're younger and hipper than her. There is no fresh-faced talent to inject this story with new energy. The two-bedroom apartment that used to feel like a triumph will start to close in on her. The city itself will close in on her. The Bean has lost its sheen. There is no wedding or promotion or baby or former lover to go back to looming in the distance, so she can only opt to do the only other option for series finales besides death: move.

This is where I am right now, having decided that the best I can do for my own personal story is to close this chapter. I think Chicagoans do a disservice to the city by constantly trying to compare it as a cleaner, friendlier, cheaper New York. Chicago shines on its own and doesn't need to be compared to anything. I will, however, allow myself this tiny indulgence and say that Chicago was my New York, if by New York we talk of this mythical vibrant setting where a hero's journey comes to full fruition. Because this period of radical transformation can obviously occur anywhere, even if pop culture is saturated with the Big Apple narrative. In fact, this period of transformation that we associate with our twenties can happen at any time in our lives and that is a freaking liberating thought: to know you can reinvent yourself even after advertisers have considered you obsolete. Especially when advertisers consider you obsolete. The first step that pushes all narratives isn't a brownstone in Brooklyn, a Vogue internship, or a high school crush that chose NYU. It's when a character makes a choice and that choice leads to change. Chicago is where I chose against safety, comfort, stability. Chicago is where I chose myself.

Members Only *Coleman*

A stage, a mirror ball, a record player.

MAN (70s, sweating) dances ecstatically. The record player plays disco music: "We Are Family."

Music ends. MAN wipes sweat from his face, neck. Drinks a clear liquid from a glass.

MAN:

Dancing! Whee-ooo! Yowza! Now that's what we used to call dancing.

Not like that whatever it is they do now. I don't even know what they do now. Don't need to know. Say what you want to about Disco, but I can tell you this: Disco... felt... good! I could dance all night. Did dance all night. Did one of those 24-hour dance marathons once. Once was enough. Sweated. Drank. Sweated some more. Drank some more. Did some drugs. And... danced.

(He dances. Stops.)

I worked at a Disco for a while. Oh, yeah.

It was after my divorce. I moved to Chicago, for what was supposed to be a dream job at the shiny new, marble-clad Ritz-Carlton in Water Tower Place on Michigan Avenue, managing their mahogany paneled dining room staffed by white gloved waiters, every one of them queer.

The job… sucked. Big time. My boss was a total jerk. The pay was terrible and the hours were soul-crushing— 80 hours a week. Salaried, no overtime. I didn't earn enough money to pay off my debts from the divorce. Worse, I got behind on child-support, which I hated.

So this waiter, guy who worked for me, told me about a way I could make money in my off hours, which meant anytime between 10 PM and 8 AM. He said a new bar had just opened on Rush Street, a few blocks away from the Ritz.

It wasn't new, exactly. The bar had been there a long time. Alfie's, it was called, a cheap watering hole for tourists, salesmen and conventioneers from Omaha or Albuquerque or wherever— a sinkhole where they could drink themselves to oblivion and pick up girls, or hire girls, so the story goes.

Well, the place was still going to be called Alfie's and nothing about the inside was going to change. Dark. Small. A tiny dance floor in one corner. A mirror ball. Oversize reverberating disco speakers. The kind of place where sunlight is not welcome— a cave off the bustling neon-lit strip that was and is Rush Street.

Overnight, Alfie's morphed from a bar where men met women to a bar where men picked up men.

> *(MAN puts on another Disco record: "It's Raining Men."*
> *Keeps volume low, under the action.*
> *MAN dances as he continues.)*

A gay bar on Rush Street in 1976 was a big deal. Gays were still universally hated, and here was this bar in the heart of Chicago's most prominent night strip. Totally in your face.

Well, Alfie's was hiring bartenders, my waiter friend said, and I knew that would be good money. Maybe I could start paying off my debts while I kept looking for a better job somewhere else. Maybe I could meet a man.

So, I went to Alfie's after work and applied.

(MAN stops dancing, turns off music.)

I never did like that song. Good to dance to, but still, just don't like it.

Turns out they weren't hiring bartenders. They had all they needed. But the "owner," Dan Reilly, (more about him later), offered me a job as bouncer.

Me. A bouncer. I wasn't a little guy back then, but I wasn't big either. Six feet, skinny, maybe 150 pounds, and about as tough as a feather. I'd never been in a fight in my life. I was hardly the guy to break up anything or stand guard over anything.

But it wasn't like that, Dan said. My job was just to keep the straights out. Yeah. Guys who had been coming to this bar for years and were coming back and had to be told that they couldn't come in anymore. Or tourists stopping by for the first time. Either way. If they were straight, they weren't welcome.

How do I do that, I asked, and Dan said I could sit and watch him do it that night and try it myself, and if I liked it, and if I showed a talent for it, then I had the job.

The pay wasn't as good as I'd hoped, but it was income, and I was desperate for cash and maybe something would open up behind the bar, so I said yes.

That night, Dan showed me what to do.

Oh, yeah, I was going to tell you more about Dan Reilly. It turned out that he wasn't really the owner. All the gay bars in town had front men who claimed to be the owner, but they weren't. They were all owned by the mob. That's how it was. Everyone knew it. Gay bars were cash business, a lot of cash, and only the mob had the connections and the muscle to run them, keep them open, and launder a hell of a lot of cash.

Reilly wasn't gay himself, though he pretended to be gay to the patrons, which was just weird. Some people called him Rita, his gay name. Guess he thought it would help seal the impression. It didn't. He even, for a while, had his quote "gay boyfriend" unquote working behind the bar— a hot young Italian kid named Billy, but Billy wasn't any more gay than Dan Reilly. I figured Billy was connected and was just working there to earn his stripes and maybe keep an eye on Reilly.

Oh, and this: Every Saturday at closing, like clockwork, this black, south-side Chicago Alderman, Clarence something, I can't recall his last name... no wait... Kelly. Cliff Kelly. Not Clarence. Clifford. Cliff Kelly. Anyway, Kelly stopped by for a drink with Dan Reilly every Saturday, just as the bar closed, and in Chicago, closing hour on Saturdays was five am. Reilly always handed a fat envelope to Cliff Kelly. That took care of the city. As for the cops, the same cop stopped by once or twice a week to take his cut. As long as the city and the cops were paid off, the bar stayed open and was never raided.

So, there I am. A bouncer. At a gay bar on Rush Street. A gay bar that used to be a straight bar. Keeping the straights out.

Now, telling gay people from straight people isn't all that hard after midnight when guys are on the prowl. You've heard about gaydar, right? It's real. I was accurate 99 percent of the time. Sometimes it was the walk, or a gesture, or clothes, or something they said, but mostly it was the eyes. I'd look into their eyes and they would look into mine and I'd know. I made a few mistakes, but not many; let in a few guys who didn't belong. They figured out pretty quickly they were in the wrong place and got out of there.

Here's how it worked, what Danny taught me that first night. A straight man or a pack of them would walk up to the door, and I would say, in a macho voice: I'm sorry sir, this is a private club now. Members only. That usually did the trick and they moved on.

Sometimes they would ask how to get a membership, and I'd say you had to be invited. Then they'd ask how to get invited, and I would say there was no way to seek an invitation. You were either invited or you weren't. And then while they were standing there, maybe a gay guy would walk up and I'd let him in past the straight guys, and I'd tell the straight guys he was a regular. Regular member. It was bullshit, but it worked.

Oh. There's this other thing. I've never talked about it. But it was a long time ago. I was young and stupid. An idiot really. But this is the way it was back then. It just was.

My first night on the door I let in three or four black guys who arrived together. They were queer as me, okay? It was obvious. But Danny came over to me and said, what was I doing letting them in? He said I couldn't let black guys in (only he didn't call 'em black, you know what I mean?). He said I couldn't let 'em in or the word would get out that blacks were welcome at

Alfie's, and then the place would fill up with blacks and the "regular" patrons would stay away.

What am I supposed to do, I asked, and he said tell them you need to see their "membership card."

And I said... I said... okay.

I should have told him to go fuck himself.

(MAN plays another record: "I Feel Love." Dances.)

Night after night, those three long summer months I worked the door at Alfie's, I turned black guys away because they didn't have membership cards, and I let white guys in because, well, because they were white. And gay, of course.

Women weren't allowed either.

In the fall I got another job, a good job, so I quit my job at the Ritz, and I quit my job at Alfie's. I'd still go back to Alfie's now and then, but it didn't matter whether I went there or some other bar, they were all the same. They were all owned by the mob, and none of them admitted blacks. After nine, ten o'clock, there was always a doorman asking for membership cards.

So.

Wanna dance?

(MAN ramps up dancing. Music swells. Lights fade.)

END

Paying the Toll at The Old Town Ale House *Harry Quinn*

It was Sammy who took me there first, sometime in—I think—1995 or maybe '96. Yeah, '96. The summer was bad, but not '95 bad— no pile up of corpses outside the morgue. Okay, that's right—we talked about the previous summer and sweating through the months, the torturous lack of AC, and the futility of box fans. And we definitely discussed the '79 blizzard and how it cost Bilandic the mayor's job, though Daley—unprepared, dismissed the '95 heatwave—had slithered away from another fuck up with his career intact. Of course, I was the only one old enough to remember the blizzard, and the only one who grew up around here, but still Sammy, a native of Kansas City, despite not knowing about Chicago's past climatological or governmental phenomena, knew the best bar in the city.

People swear by this bar, he said.

What's so special?

Hard to say.

He tried. Talked about the generations of drunks and aspiring improv comics that flocked to the oasis on North Avenue, maybe the last spot in the neighborhood to avoid gentrification. This we loved, thinking ourselves beyond reproach, not understanding our own role in the transitions Old Town, Lincoln Park, Lakeview, and Wicker Park were undergoing. Years later, we'd be the ones crying when our favorite boho café became a Starbucks and the hip dives pulled their last pints. Fucking gentrification, we'd say, still not seeing ourselves as the first wave that ushered in the Lululemons.

Outside the bar, I saw my cousin. She was with some friends, all of them dolled up and ready for a night of watching their drinks and dodging roofies.

Where ya goin'?

Old Town Ale House. You?

She named a club I'd never heard of but could tell was not anything like where we were going. Sammy and Bill, perpetually single like me, were disappointed that we didn't get invited to join the gaggle of young women.

That about sums us up, I said. She goes to dance, I go to drink.

We might've joined them, Bill offered, though his voice betrayed awareness that there was no way we'd fit with them or the club they were heading to. Just look how we were dressed.

The layout was as it should be. Bar to the west. Tables available. Comfortable. Well-worn. Pinball machine. A juke box devoid of the music my cousin and her girlfriends were dancing to. No shots allowed, which was fine by us. Sammy had been on a scotch bender, and while he had not the resources to binge salt malt, he—like the rest of us—regarded the practice of slamming hard liquor as one reserved for amateurs who needed to get the burn of alcohol over with. You don't do a shot of scotch, he said, rolling his eyes at the very notion. A connoisseur savors their poison. Even mid-shelf scotch was to be enjoyed slowly.

Three, four, five rounds of draft beer and, I think, Famous Grouse. Something along those lines. It hurt, but after a few rounds you stop noticing. Caring.

I need to piss, said Bill inelegantly. But he wasn't gone long. Can't go in that toilet, he said. Oh, right. Pee shy. I'd been with him in line for the one working urinal at Liar's Club and he'd chickened out as he got close enough to feel the weight of men behind him wordlessly urging him to c'mon already, man, hurry the fuck up.

What are you gonna do, hold it?

Be back.

Bill exited the bar and went in search of a friendlier, more private facility, and Sammy decided to give the Old Town a little more of his money. I'm tapped, I said. Get you back next week? Check. Good guy, that Sammy.

But we ought to have cut it off. Sammy was good for a few rounds, but there's that point where we all get too stupid, aggressive, or maudlin. And this was that point. This round. And, yep, there went Sammy on and on about his loveless existence—he, like many of us idiots, felt entitled to love— and the girl he had a thing for. I saw her yesterday. She gave me a hug. That's gotta mean something.

71

Not really.

You don't think?

No, I don't.

Fuck.

Sorry.

I'm... I'm...

It's alright, man. Just talk to her.

I can't.

Well, then...

I'm fucked.

Yeah.

Another round.

Better not.

No, I guess not.

Here comes Bill.

HEY GUYS!

Success?

Yeah, the diner let me use their bathroom.

Congrats.

One more round?

Eh...

My treat.

Okay.

From there it gets fuzzy. Nothing bad, no bar fighting or public vomiting. Just sluggish and sleepy and see you tomorrow and back to the couch because the bed is one room away and it was enough just getting up the stairs. And the toll to be paid the next morning. Fried bacon and eggs, black coffee, three aspirin.

Since that night, I've been over to the Ale House a few more times, each one of them memorable, though not in any glorious mythical sense. Nothing one would read in a Bukowski story. Just social drinking and lovely conversation with lovely people, some of them receptive to the bar's charm, some marveling at the art on the walls depicting regulars, legendary Chicago reprobates, the briefly famous nude Sarah Palin. But not everyone took to the Ale House. No accounting for taste. Maybe the grit and divier aspects are a turn off, though there are worse dives in town. Maybe the décor is not to their liking. Not everyone likes to see a bare-assed Blagojevich. Maybe the

No Shots rule and lack of dance music are a deal breaker. Maybe they go at the wrong time and meet a true regular, not the Saturday night crowd. Maybe that turns them off. There's slumming, and then there's *slumming*. Maybe they just don't see the value in what is one of the last honest institutions in the north side of Chicago, housed a stone's throw from nail salons and upscale dining, a mere mile from the most ostentatious Whole Foods imaginable. And while I've never been a regular at the Ale House, I smile when I pass by. Knowing it's there makes me somewhat less apprehensive about my own slow march toward physical decline. If that place can survive, there's hope for all of us. And I hope to raise one more glass at the bar before I pay my last toll.

Big Suchir   *Vimi Bajaj*

I went into Big Suchir to get channas while the twins waited in the car with their big sister. I ended up picking out some frozen foods like samosas and butter chicken. Meena Ben would never make non-veg, and I was too lazy to bother cooking from scratch. A Japanese couple, both of them slight of build and formally dressed, followed me in, picked out a masala packet, paid and left, speaking quietly to themselves in their native tongue. On the glass counter, near the entrance was always a plate of sweetmeats, and an agarbati stand with lighted incense sticks as if a puja had just been performed and the offerings made plentifully available to any and all patrons.

In the fridge section were homemade pickles like jalapeño mixed with carrots in fermented rye, fried pakoras (don't know how good those can be, I thought), shrikhand, a sweet liquidy concoction which had made me choke silently at a friend's house almost a decade ago. All things that could have been made and probably were, by women with names like Meena Ben or Kanta Ben or Laxmi Ben.

The store manager Rakesh, a hefty fellow of about thirty, greeted me as I came in without looking up from his calculations. The store was sunny and warm. I quickly eyed every aisle, bargaining with myself about the salty snacks and the sweets for my autistic son (he had a real sweet tooth, unlike his twin brother who preferred cakes and cookies and donuts to Indian sweets) but settled on the frozen samosas, a thing we had not had in a while, a weekend pleasure with cardamom tea.

Some people are so well suited to what they do that their very bearing and setup evokes their profession. Rakesh, for instance, was a born shop wala, gold chain around his neck, well fed physique, a scrunched-up face only a mother could love. He wore gemstones on each finger, and sat with one leg

74

crossed, the bottom of his foot obscenely face-up, on his high stool behind the counter, balancing accounts, punching numbers into the calculator, running a very tight ship with one lone employee. I had seen her in the back, usually behind the plate glass counter which displayed sweetmeats like chum chums and barfi and fried snacks. She was about twenty-five and very thin, and I'd seen her many times walk the entire length of the shop, pushing a fold-up trolley, the metal kind with two wheels, the kind you needed to tilt back to get going on uneven surfaces.

She said hi, and I found myself stopping for her greeting, as if it was another grocery item to be checked off on my list. She stood in a flamingo pink shirt, unobtrusive, dragging a flour sack which had the words "chakki atta whole wheat flour" in the front and a picture of a village woman in traditional clothing before a hand mill, grinding flour the old-fashioned way on a stone pedestal.

A woman in a business suit came in. She looked out of place, not just because she was Caucasian, but because she was very well put together. The sales clerk asked: "Do you need some help?"

"I'm looking for red lentils," the woman said.

The sales clerk, unused to people using the English term for dals, whispered "red lentils" to herself several times needing help finding them, and Rakesh finally had to come out to locate the masoor dal and listen to the lady complain.

When it was my turn to pay, I wondered how much he'd overcharged me/her.

In my rush to get my groceries, I had meant to acknowledge her further, the worker, the only employee, with a cheerful hello, as we had done many times before. But the well-heeled woman, obviously wanting to try new culinary recipes, blocked the aisle. I looked the girl's way once more amidst the shuffle of bodies in the lentil and spice aisle and managed to catch her eye. Before I could say anything, the girl sent over a meek and yet familiar hello of recognition and was just as swiftly taken away by the stubborn customer in her relentless search for red lentils.

Inhale Chicago *Cajetan Sorich*

I work at a spa in the Gold Coast. I've worked there for almost four years. That means I was hired when I was eighteen, and that means when I was first hired, I tried hard to be a good employee, due to an irrational fear of being fired. Sometimes, I thought for hours after I left about some small mistake that I made, fearing that I forgot or miscalculated something, or everything. Sometimes, when I arrived for my Wednesday closing shift after school, I would take a cloth and cleaning spray from the spa dispensary and dust the delicate glass shelves in the boutique and behind the desk, even if there was no dust.

Nowadays I don't give one little tiny itty bitty fuck about this stupid goddamn job. For my past twenty shifts in a row, I have arrived stoned. Even if I don't want to get stoned, I make sure to come to work stoned to honor the pact I made with myself to disrespect my job in as many secret ways as possible. Secretly disrespecting my job is a form of self-care, a way to respect myself. Because—not to be insensitive to corporations, as they are legally people—fuck this corporation. It's a barre studio with Buddha statues. They promote wellness as a lifestyle, but in that skinny, shameful 80s through 2010s way I've had to train my neural pathways to unlearn. They let rich clients abuse us, but barely pay us above minimum wage. My covenant to not care allows me to enjoy the twenty-to-thirty hours a week—that's 11.9%-17% of my precious and fleeting life—that I spend working at the spa. I need the money, but I need to defend myself against my position as Inhale's Little Bitch. Hence: the bong.

Every Friday I start work at 5:45 AM, because the first fitness class starts promptly at 6:00. I wake up at 4:50 to catch the Division bus by 5:05. Getting up at dawn, which during my worst insomnia bouts is when I may finally be getting to sleep, makes me sad. It's weird, frankly, to have to disorient my body for a corporation that doesn't care about me.

When my alarm goes off I am usually eating donuts or spaghetti in some strange dream, and because at 5 AM I am still half dreaming, I usually taste donuts or spaghetti until I go outside and taste the bitter-cold Chicago winter instead. After my alarm, I stuff whatever lunch I packed the night before and ground-coffee to make at work into my backpack. My roommate's boyfriend is a barista and he keeps bringing us bags of fancy coffee, but the catch is that they're always whole-bean. For a while I used a regular-old blender to grind it, but since then I have grown up (I stole a coffee grinder from Target, just walked right out with it). Since there's no time on Friday mornings, on Thursday nights I grind a serving of coffee and twist it into the corner of a grocery bag saved from previous shopping trips. After I'm all packed, I rip the bong that me and my roommates have been sharing for two years but have not once cleaned. I've recently decided that every time I smoke from the bong I am probably also getting high on whatever ancient lichens are growing inside of it.

At work I am an intentional fuck-up. As our fitness classes preach, I am mindful, but mindful of screwing this place over as much as I can without getting fired. We're supposed to count our cash drawers at the start and end of our shift, but I only pretend to count mine and then copy-and-paste the same amount from the previous shift report. I usually serve as the manager on duty, and if I'm working with someone I know also doesn't care about the job, I tell them they don't have to count. The two drawers are supposed to be at $200, but for three weeks now they've each only had around $174, and I suspect that the discrepancy has something to do with my negligence. But I cannot, per my covenant, care.

I am actually pretty good at my job. Well, I have the capacity to be good at it. Aside from one other desk-person, I've worked here longer than any of the other desk lackies and all of the higher management. I'm a master at the computer program we use for the appointments and accounts; my boss calls me from her office to ask me how to do things. Of course, empirically, I am a terrible, terrible employee, but it takes someone who is deeply familiar with their job to succeed at being as shitty as I am without getting caught. I know exactly the duties I can get away with not doing, and how to fake the ones I need to do. Little tricks. I closed last Tuesday night and to make it look like I counted my drawer, I recorded in my shift report that we were at five cents less than the start of the shift. That way, when someone counts it later and finds that it was not actually five cents off, they'd figure that I miscounted a nickel. No big deal, the important part is that I'm counting my drawer. Who the fuck cares about five cents?

Sadly, though, most of the others who work at this damn spa do. Another MOD, who, like me, has worked at this Gold Coast shit castle for over three years and makes $13 an hour, replied to my shift report *from home* suggesting I miscounted. This dang woman, this twenty-five-year-old person with a complex and fertile internal and external life, with mounds of her very own fears and hopes to overcome each and every day, was at home thinking about the damn nickels in the front desk cash register.

This is why I have the covenant.

I have to preserve my energy for *real* problems, and $13 an hour isn't worth giving nickel-level attention to the health of a stingy business.

The corporation certainly does not give to us. And along with being selfish bastards, they're shockingly poor at running the company. In the past two years, we've had five different spa directors. In the past year, three different front desk managers. I've liked most of these people, but I couldn't care less about seeing them come and go. I am, however, baffled by the fact that corporate hasn't tried to slow this rapid turnover. The spa director is the highest administrative job at each of the spa's locations; most people stay in positions like this for at least five years. Has corporate not realized how shitty they must be for their spa directors to be quitting every six months?

Again, I've liked most of my bosses. They've been funny, sweet, supportive. Two of them have made me cry, though. Once, one of them got so angry that they took the phone and slammed it with about all of their might against the desk, over and over again. One of them, every time I came in, told me that I didn't fit the brand and to go brush my hair (if I take a brush to my hair it turns into an ugly frizz puff, but okay). She told me I looked sloppy and to sit up straighter. It was during her reign, actually, that I stopped trying to be a helpful, good employee and decided to bullshit all of the things I was supposed to be doing.

Readers who know what I look like: please close your eyes and imagine for a moment that I am extending my arms up and out, diagonally from my ears, making a peace sign with each hand. Take a deep breath, really connect with and check in with how your body and mind feel and repeat this mantra while imagining my mouth moving with the words, their sounds vibrating in my throat chakra and nourishing yours: I am not a crook. (I'm actually at work typing this, at this very moment, and to access an accurate description of the Nixon pose, I did the gesture myself, which concerned my fellow GUEST EXPERIENCE ASSOCIATE, who asked, "is everything okay?") The spa is the crook; the clients are the crooks. Profiting off of the false wellness of women by telling them that barre classes will give them round, firm asses is crooked. Yoga classes taught by fitness buffs in a city studio with a fake gong are crooked. Selling shirts by a brand called Spiritual Gangster that say things like "dope soul" and, my favorite, "the G in me recognizes the G in you," this is crooked. My only power at this place lies in stealing from the lost-and-found, coming in stoned, and taking grotesquely long breaks.

Nickels are abstract, wellness and fitness are cons, and being instilled with the idea that we should care—from home—about the amount of money in the spa's cash drawers is… honestly kind of tragic. Time may be abstract, too, but it's scarier to lose than money. Most of the people who work the desk here don't realize that by giving their care so wholly to this place, they are losing parts of themselves, too. They've been conned into thinking they somehow owe their strongest and utmost efforts to any job that hires them, but that's not true. Not when it's a place like this, where nobody cares about you.

It's not that I'm spoiled or opposed to working hard for the greater good of an establishment outside of myself, it's actually quite the opposite. It's just that I only want to work hard for places that I consider to be good and vital. I have a second job as a writing tutor, and I give my utmost care to it. I became a lead tutor after working there for one semester because I work hard. I spend extra time with any student who asks. I have a folder that I carry with me that holds a stack of resources I've compiled on everything from paragraph structure to introducing formal sources in an essay. My little sister Emma actually teases me about it.

"I've been so busy, Emma, I'm dying."

"Aw man. You're gonna have to quit the Writing Center."

"The writing center??"

"The WRITING CENTER??" She mocks me, laughs. "I just wanted to see the look on your face."

I will give myself and my time to practice what I love and to help people. On the other hand, I will disrespect the spa at every opportunity, to protect myself and save my energy. At the Writing Center, I will be serious and focused for hours, if necessary. At the spa, I just try to have fun.

On Saturday nights, I close with Emma, who was hired a little over a year ago. A few Saturdays back we took turns hitting her weed pen in the steam room and then ordered Rosati's pizza to the lobby. We aren't allowed to eat at the desk, but when all our bosses leave, we tend to either order pizza or microwave an obscene amount of pizza rolls.

Emma is nineteen and has been living with me since she was seventeen. I also moved to the city when I was seventeen. We both graduated young because we have summer birthdays and didn't turn eighteen until after our senior years ended. In July 2013 I found a room in Humboldt Park, stuffed all of my belongings into a garbage bag, and asked my friend to drive me to the Aurora Metra. Emma and I grew up in Yorkville, IL, where the senior prank, multiple years, was douchebag boys driving their tractors to school instead of their cars, and this is why I used to be paranoid of losing my job. I saved money frantically to ensure that if I did get fired, I'd have buffer time before having to hang my head and move back to my way too Catholic dad's house (he kicked me out for refusing to go to mass) near the tractor jocks who spent 11.9%-17% of their high school careers calling me a lesbian because I was too cool for their small brains to comprehend.

I still would absolutely *die* if I had to move back to Yorkville, and I can't afford to lose my spa job. Unfortunately, I can't afford to serve my job, either. As I said, I need to save my energy for *real* problems. I need to collect and preserve my kindness for people who actually need it, people who I love, like Emma.

Emma, who everyone believed was arrested in the school parking lot for selling hashish, had a more comical reputation—and motive for leaving Yorkville—than I. The hashish salesperson thing is a rumor (and if it's not, I will be retroactively angry that she did not share her hashish with me), but she did pull some concerning stunts. For one, Emma was suspended for biting a kid. She also, in her freshman year, when I was a senior, swallowed my mom's entire bottle of Klonopin before riding the bus to school. By third period an ambulance was weeeooooing outside. High school-reputation-wise, that'll get ya. Emma has attempted suicide two times since, one of which was very bloody and one of which was on New Year's Eve of 2018—yo-ho-ho and a bottle of vodka (and Xanax)—both of which I was there for and had to Bernie her to the hospital.

Though she missed the rest of her freshman year, Emma graduated with 5.0/4.0 weighted GPA because she got straight A's in all honors classes. I graduated with somewhere near a 4.0, but it's a less impressive accomplishment compared to Emma not only because I got lower grades, but because Emma balanced excelling in school with fucking up all of the time. On my 20th birthday, when Emma was 17 but still in Yorkville, I got a late-night call from a 630 (Yorkville area code) phone number and assumed it was someone calling to tell me happy birthday. I answered and a man said, "Hello, this is officer Tartaglione from Kendall country, I'm here with Emma Pavlovic, are you her mother, Jane Weber?"

I didn't hesitate. "Yes I am. What's going on?"

Tartaglione told me that he found Emma and another minor, Alex Rodriguez, in an abandoned subdivision, outside and naked. "What would you like me to do, ma'am?"

Fake sigh, fake motherly stoicism. "Just send her home, I'll talk to her."

"Is it okay to have Alex Rodriguez drive her back, or would you like me to take her?"

I told Tartaglione that "I know the boy," and to have him take her home (god forbid a police car dropped Emma off at my dad's). He reiterated to me that Emma, my daughter, was—despite being at the age of consent—naked with Alex Rodriguez. Real sigh, I was disturbed by the man's preoccupation with my sister's sexuality. "Thank you, officer. I'll take care of it."

I don't understand how she didn't get in trouble, because I do not sound like a woman old enough to have a 17-year-old daughter, and Emma and Alex Rodriguez were trashed. She told me that she was sitting on the trunk of Alex's car holding a bottle of vodka when the cop car pulled up and she quickly slid off, opened the passenger door, and tossed it under the seat. The cop asked her what she threw into the car, and she said it was water. Stupid damn Tartaglione was so damn preoccupied with my little sister's sex-life he didn't realize that she was drunk on a vulgar amount of, probably Skol, vodka.

Since then we've moved onto bigger and better things: stealing Lululemon pants from the lost-and-found and taking two-hour breaks (after management leaves) to sleep, steam, and, in my case, use the fitness studio to dance. We are also quite good at hanging up on clients mid-call and pretending that the connection was lost, and calling 7:45 PM massage appointments to lie and tell them that their sessions are cancelled because their therapist had an emergency so that Emma and I can go home early. When I work with someone other than Emma, I merely pretend to do all of my job duties.

The moral of this anecdote is that Emma is smart. She's resourceful in unconventional ways and confident in her choices. Emma, like me, is selective about what she gives her energy to because she has even less than I do. In her lack of respect for our job, there is the same subconscious protest toward capitalism and abuse from the elite that drives my lack of respect. This protest makes us asshole employees, but in the eyes of the therapists and spa attendants, we are the most kind and supportive people there. The first thing she and I say to new massage therapists and aestheticians is "let me know if you need anything," because part of being a dick to corporations is acknowledging its employees as human beings with needs.

I mentioned earlier how waking up at dawn to serve this corporation makes me sad, but I did not yet elaborate on how the clients are salt on the wound. Most of the fitness members cannot bear to stop at the desk and give me their name so I can check them in. They expect me to know their names after seeing them once or twice, but barely any of them know mine. They struggle deeply to comply with the basic process of checking into a class, but they often expect me to solve problems for them that are totally irrelevant to my job title and our relationship. Last week, a woman asked me if I could charge her card $10 and then give her $10 from the cash drawer. I said no, because we're not a fucking bank, you entitled either young professional or heir, and she said: "I need cash to get my car out of the lot I parked in, and I only have my credit card. What am I going to do?"

What am I going to do?

This thinking that "the spa is a bank because I can get people to do whatever I want because I'm rich" is a prominent theme among clients. Once, another regular brought in a bag of dimes (*a bag of dimes*) and asked us to count them and give her cash in exchange for them. And these people wonder why they sometimes don't receive confirmation calls the day before their appointments.

These types of clients are ignorant, but at least they're not vicious. There are indeed vicious and crooked clients, many of which have made it onto a list of "bad clients" that we keep behind the desk. One of them, a realtor named Melinda Jakovich, has her photo on the list like a big fat shiny headshot. Melinda tends to leave without paying and deny it when we call her and ask her to please, please just fucking pay up.

Last week, a woman snuck her friend into a yoga class without paying and ignored me when I said her name three incredibly audible times as she walked out. These clients are little mirrors of the corporation: rich, crooked, and clinging to their money.

I'm nice to clients, but only if they're nice to me. I have interesting connections with some of them. One is a professor at my university, and one I bumped into at Nando's Peri Peri on my birthday and since then, I feel like we're friends. I found out that one client, Kasey, grew up with my brother Simon who died a few years ago. She said that they took drivers ed together. Every time I check Kasey in for class, my eyes water. Even Emma is exceptionally warm to the nice clients. I will say, though, that sometimes I take offense to a client with a nice attitude because I know they expect me to match their pep-level, and in doing so they are harvesting my emotional labor, which I consider a miniature form of abuse. And sometimes—usually— they're just trying to manipulate me. And sometimes they're annoying. They don't know my name, but they waste my time by asking how I am. They call and say, "Hello, this is so-and-so calling," as if I'm supposed to know who they are. Though, admittedly, I often do know who they are because I've worked here for so long. I usually pretend I don't remember, though.

To preserve myself, I can't be vulnerable to these people. And even if I had the energy to cater to the emotions of the rude clients, I wouldn't. We keep notes in the system under clients' names, many of which say things like "made me cry on 10/24/16." Another example: "guest may 'find' issues to complain about in hopes of receiving discounted services. May be insulting, aggressive, and verbally demeaning, handle with care." Once, on the phone, a woman asked me to describe each one of our estheticians to her, and in an attempt to gently set a boundary I said that I didn't know what they all looked like. She yelled at me. "How the FUCK am I supposed to know who I had last time?" Jesus, I don't know, use your memory? Write it down? See if our website has cute little bios with pictures of our therapists? Give your name, and ask if we have a record of who you've seen for facials instead of calling me and asking me to describe 20 different women to you in depth?

Once, the day after Christmas, I booked a man, Robert Jimenez, with the "wrong" esthetician. After the incident, the following note was made: "BEWARE guest is very rude and demanding. Please proceed with caution and know that guest has a tendency to be verbally abusive."

I know what it's like to hate life, and I care about others' pain, but if I can manage to be kind to people—even when they screw up my coffee order—then so can rich people. I used to give people like Robert Jimenez the benefit of the doubt. A man who is so mean the day after Christmas must have had a horrible, lonely holiday. He's in pain and stressed about his important business stuff is all, and he's so sad that he can't help but abuse young women working the desk at a spa. I told myself that all of these rich and abusive clients are just struggling so hard that they have lost their ability to withhold swearing at me for not knowing which therapist they last saw. But then I realized that this assumption stems from childhood fables that kindergarten teachers told me so that I would develop a sense of empathy and perhaps develop my critical thinking ability. *There are reasons behind his behavior, he is hurt and projecting his pain.* Yeah sure, there're reasons why he's cruel, but it's not because he's sad. It's because he's a spoiled goddamn rich man-brat who can do whatever the fuck he wants. This makes more sense than the secret-hurt theory, because too many of these rich people are cruel for them all to be violently hurting inside.

The ol' empathetic lens is important, and in many situations I'm sure it is correct. But the fables were taught also to mold me into a proper worker under capitalism. To indoctrinate me to be one of the meek who suffer at the hands of people who abuse them and damn them to a life of material problems and scarcity but shouldn't stand up for themselves or question anything, and instead value being meek because after they die they'll inherit the earth. Except I'm an atheist, and I've read the *Genealogy of Morals*. And Marx. The way religion is opium for the poor, being taught that the clients at the spa are just mean because they have tough lives is like opium for being shit on by people who weren't happy with their $200 facial. They're spoiled.

As I mentioned, I know what it's like to hate life. I also understand pain. My parents are neglectful and always have been, one of my siblings is dead, one of them isn't healthy. These things have made me weaker and broken in many regards, but I'm okay with it. I think grappling with bunk parents, the death of a sibling, and completely financially supporting myself as a teenager has at least made me, in some ways, smarter. And so when I go to work high and fuck around the whole time, I don't think I'm just a jackass kid who doesn't know how to respect authority or be responsible. I'm just trying to preserve myself. I'm nearly always hurting, and since Simon died, I am hyper-aware that my life is short and my time is ticking, and I don't want to spend this time giving the small bit of energy I have left after seeing my brother's dead body, or the fat dripping out of the deep cuts in Emma's arms, to Inhale Chicago.

When Robert Jimenez found out that I didn't book him with his preferred esthetician, I made the mistake of explaining myself. I told him that I didn't hear him request her on the phone, and he yelled at me. I smiled and he told me—and I quote—that I don't take life seriously and demanded an apology. He made me pull my boss out of a yoga class and as he relayed my atrocious behavior to my boss, pointed at my face and said, "look at her, look at her smirk."

Wrigley Field: A Love Story
Nick Francone

When I am dead and buried, I will probably be most remembered as being a Cubs fan over everything else in my life, and that is ok. That fandom was cemented when I was a ten-year-old boy on what would turn out to be a memory burn of an afternoon at the friendly confines.

I was already falling in love. Bill Buckner, Bruce Sutter, and Rick Reuschel were my heroes. My dad lived in Ohio, so my two Uncles, Dan and John, would take me to my share of ball games. I had no idea what laid in store for me as we headed out to the ballpark one fine Sunday afternoon.

In the late 70s the Cubs would routinely get murdered by the Phillies, and this day looked to be no different. They got down five runs early and my uncles put down just as many Old Styles to drown their sorrows, as it looked like it was going to be another typical Cub loss. Then out of nowhere the northside nine started to make a comeback. Somehow, miraculously they scored three in the ninth to win the ball game.

The place (all 8,000 of us that were there that afternoon) went bonkers. My uncles both decided after a win like that they had to grab a cold one before heading back on the Red Line. Unlike today, back in the late 70s there were basically four bars in the Wrigleyville area. Murphy's Bleachers, The Cubby Bear, Bernie's, and the Sports Corner.

They chose the Sports Corner, which back then was small, dank, and dark. It has since been remodeled to look like a TGI Friday's. The patrons in the bar were carrying the party-like atmosphere from the park into the bar. The music was blaring, people were dancing, and then it happened.

Two rather inebriated young ladies decided to jump on top of the bar and dance. The mostly male crowd, almost in unison, started chanting "take it off, take it off!" It was at this point my Uncle John looked at my Uncle Dan and questioned whether my ten-year-old eyes should be subjected to what was about to happen.

My Uncle Dan, and remember this was 1979 and, well, it was just a different time, shrugged his shoulders and said to my Uncle John, "He's going to see them eventually," and it was at that exact moment the two young ladies removed their tops. My eyes got as big as saucers as I, for the first time in my life, saw up close the female form.

The die was cast, and my love of the Cubs (and of the female form) was embedded into my DNA. From 1977 until 2019, I went to at least one game a year and in many years 15-20 games per season. I saw firsthand how the seedy area that Wrigley Field resided in turned into the Disneyland atmosphere it is today.

Sure, things are probably better now. But something feels lost along with more of the old bars and shops from my youth going away. Many of the little guys got squeezed out over the years (I cried a tear when Yum Yum Donuts got knocked down). Strange Cargo lasted as long as it could before moving to Andersonville. When lights were installed in 1988, it was a total game changer. Now instead of getting ripped at happy hour after the game, you could close out the bars at 2 AM.

I still get nostalgic when I go to the park, even at fifty-one. Even after all the Tribune Company did before, and the Rickets family has done now, to change the experience, they cannot take away what it is like to get off the train at Addison and still feel like that ten-year-old. I know all the tricks (enter out into the alley when getting out of the train station and not onto Addison with all the newbies). I know what bars serve the best food and which ones are the best places to meet friends. I know which spots are the best for a pre-game urination.

Wrigley Field is a different experience depending on what day of the week you are there and where you are sitting. The bleachers are for the college kids looking to drink, hookup, and maybe watch a little baseball. On the rare occasions I sit there, I feel as old as Methuselah.

I usually sit in what was once called the 200 section (in 2019 they changed the seating sections, much to my chagrin). I try to sit in the first seven rows, so I am not behind a pole. I contend that and the old 500 section are where the hardy fans sit. On a Friday afternoon, it is a party atmosphere. On a Sunday, it is parents with their kids in tow. But no matter what time or day, or where I am sitting, I still get that same feeling when I walk in and smell those onions being grilled at the hot dog stands inside the park.

I try to go to at least one game a year by myself. I get my scorecard and pencil and watch the opposing team take batting practice and just look out at the wonder that is this ballpark nestled into a working-class neighborhood. It truly is a miracle that we have this gem of a ballpark still standing, and not bulldozed and the team moved to Rosemont.

I was at a game a couple of years ago. I was by myself sitting down the right field line keeping score. In front of me was a dad with his three daughters. The girls were all under sixteen years of age. And each one of them had their own scorecards and were keeping score as well as asking intelligent baseball questions. They were not on their phones, they were sitting there taking in the beauty of this great game and this great park. I know that is in no way typical of most teenage behavior, but it warmed my middle-aged heart and gave me hope that, even after I am gone, Wrigley Field will still be there, and the love for the park and the team will be passed on to future generations.

Welcome to the Bigs *Wayne Lerner*

Fast ball. Down the middle. Crack! Hard liner to the third baseman. Heck! Out again.

It was the summer of 1957, and I was spending most of my time playing baseball in the alley. Our field was defined by the garbage cans on the left and right protecting wooden garages where the owners' beat up Chevy or Buick lived. No foreign cars were ever seen on our streets unless the driver was from another neighborhood and had gotten lost. The cans were a challenge as they were constantly filled with so much rotting trash that the flies buzzing around would interfere with catching a lazy fly ball. Home plate was the wall of the tire factory that emitted the smell of burning rubber from early morning to late at night. After an inning or two, we got used to it. No outfield fence, just the end of the block which seemed to be a 100-miles away.

If we didn't play ball in the alleys, we played pinners against the front-stoop with a pinkie or fastpitch against the factory wall. What we didn't want to do is hit our only league into the yard of Mr. Hardwick, who had Baron, the meanest German Shepherd imaginable on patrol. Baron drooled with desire when he saw us come near, the dream of tearing off a piece of our skin or even a finger or two making him crazy.

One June day, my mother got a call from Uncle Howard. He worked at the Coady Brothers Meat Packing Company located in the Fulton Market District. Uncle Howard knew that I loved baseball and the White Sox and asked if he could take me to my first professional ball game at Comiskey Park. I was so excited when I heard the news that I ran around the apartment whooping and hollering.

Coady Brothers had season's tickets, which Uncle Howard frequently used. I didn't know it at the time, but the company supplied all of the meat to Comiskey Park. Thus, the brothers had access to the Owners' private dining area, the Bard's Room, and a special relationship with the owners, manager and coaches of the team.

Early the following Saturday, we got into my father's 1955 Chevrolet to meet Uncle Howard at the Market. He had stopped there to prepare a special order to take with him to the game. Uncle Howard was putting a large brown wrapper package in the trunk of his white Bonneville as we rolled to a stop. Much to my surprise, I saw my cousins, Myra and Alan, in their dad's car. I didn't know they were going, but I was thrilled. I liked them a lot and now knew I would not have to talk to Uncle Howard all by myself for the whole game. I jumped in their car so excited that I don't think I even said goodbye to my parents.

We went south on Halsted until we reached 35th and then turned left. Comiskey Park started to come into view, slowly flooding the front windshield with its arched windows and immense, white structure. Uncle Howard pulled into the lot right next to the stadium and parked near gate three, the home plate entrance.

Uncle Howard greeted a man in a blue suit and handed him the brown wrapper package.

"This is for Al," he said. "Please make sure to give it to him before the game." We went through the turnstiles and began to climb a large set of stairs. As we approached the main concourse, the smells permeated our senses. Popcorn, caramel corn, hotdogs, french fries, hamburgers, grilled onions, beer, all of it prepared in anticipation of the big crowd that day, as the Sox were playing the Yankees. The Sox were in second place, four games out of first.

We walked through the entry portal and, as we did, the field revealed itself before our eyes. I was overwhelmed by the enormity of the stadium.

"I knew it was big but not this big," I said to my cousins. They just laughed. "It's your first time, isn't it? Every time we come here, we get the same feeling."

My eyes followed the long main aisle that separated the lower boxes from the upper ones. The box seats surrounded the entire field until they met the outfield walls. I could see the outfield seats stretch from the left field foul pole to the one in right. A towering second deck spanned the entire park, except for centerfield. The upper deck seemed to be hundreds of feet high, reaching almost to the sky. In centerfield, above the bleacher seats, was the main scoreboard.

Uncle Howard's seats were in box 58, the first row below the main aisle, just to the left of the screen, right behind home plate. I was in awe. I stood there, immobile, taking in the sights, smells and sounds, oblivious to everyone around me.

I had brought my mitt to the park in the hopes that I could catch a foul ball. Given where our seats were, there was a slim chance that could happen. I would have to be ready as any foul ball coming towards us would be a piercing line drive off the player's bat.

"Are you ok?" Myra said. "What's the matter with you?"

"He's fine, Myra." Alan laughed. "Leave him alone. He's gone into that dream world of his. He thinks he's a major leaguer. He'll wake up when the hot dog guy comes around."

I watched the players taking batting practice and playing pepper along the sidelines. Some of them were doing stretching exercises on the field as both teams were warming up for the day's competition. I was so close that I could hear them talking to one another. Sometimes they would swear out loud if they missed a ball thrown or pitched to them in the batting cage. Every so often, they would spit out this black stuff from the wad in their mouth and then go back to chewing whatever it was.

Gross, I thought. But I guess this is what you do when you get to the majors. I wonder if this is something they learn in the minor leagues. Gross.

We saw the hot dog guy and were getting ready to eat when Uncle Howard tapped me on the arm. "Come with me, I've got something to show you," he said. Something's up, I thought, but I had no idea what. Was I going into the Bard's Room to meet the owner? Or was Uncle Howard going to introduce me to one of the retired players who were now working for the Sox?

We went to the aisle just to our left, took a right turn down the steps and approached the brick wall separating the seating area from the playing field. On my left was the White Sox dugout, along the third base side. The Yankees, the dreaded Bronx Bombers, were warming up on the first base side.

As we drew closer to the wall, I saw the metal gate that led from the seats to the field. We stood there for a moment when an Andy Frain usher came over to us. After shaking Uncle Howard's hand, he opened the gate. We walked onto the field where Uncle Howard introduced me to, of all people, the manager of the White Sox, Al Lopez. He was talking to his coaches about the Sox lineup.

My heart stopped.

Al Lopez! I'm on the field at Comiskey! And he's going to talk to me! I thought.

My hands got sweaty and my throat was dry. Don't faint, I said to myself. This will never happen again!

"Al," said Uncle Howard, "this is my nephew, Wayne. He's never been to a professional baseball game before but he's a big Sox fan. I thought we should give him a little thrill."

Mr. Lopez just smiled at me and said, "We will certainly show him a good time today because we're going to beat the Yankees badly."

I nodded and smiled but couldn't talk, paralyzed with excitement.

Mr. Lopez called over to one of his coaches who walked me into the dugout. There was Little Looey, Luis Aparicio, Nellie Fox, and even Billy Pierce. I could barely breathe. This was a surreal moment for me, seven years old, in Comiskey Park, in the dugout, talking to my heroes. I knew that I would never, ever again have this opportunity to be around professional ballplayers. I was a chubby, nerdy, average athlete who would never graduate from the alley league.

All of a sudden, one of the younger players grabbed me by the jersey and said, "Follow me. We have a job to do." He guided me to the outfield where there were dozens of baseballs from batting practice lying on the field. "Your job, with these other boys, is to pick up all the balls and put them in the baskets."

I learned later that the other kids were the sons of the coaches or the players who were used to having access to the field and interacting with all the players. This was certainly not the case for this kid from the west side.

I started to pick up the balls and put them in the basket. Every so often, I stopped to look around the park as people took their seats. I imagined what it would be like to be a ball player, standing in the outfield, awaiting the pitch and getting ready to move at a moment's notice. No sir. I was not in the alley trying to get away from Baron the boy eating dog or the hundreds of garbage can flies.

I was in my little dreamland again when I heard a voice coming from my left. There was "Jungle Jim" Rivera waving off everyone so he could catch the batting practice flyball. An outfielder, normally, today, he was playing first base.

"Hey, kid," he growled, "Wanna catch one?"

I stood frozen. I looked around the double deck park teeming with people. The sounds ringing in my ears and the smell of the grass and the food overwhelming my senses.

"Kid," he hollered, "get your ass over here 'cause there's another ball comin' off the bat."

I ran next to Rivera knowing, with trepidation, that there was no way I could make that catch. My eyes were terrible, and I couldn't judge where the ball might land. In the alleys and on the fields at Columbus Park, I played first base because all I had to do was catch the occasional pop up and the throws from the infielders. I could do that, but this?

Time after time, fly balls were hit and, as the balls came down, Rivera moved away to try and let me make the catch. Time after time, I missed. Actually, I was fortunate that I didn't get beaned trying to catch the major league fly balls.

Finally, Rivera grabbed my Sox jersey and pulled me next to him. We stood there and watched a ball rise from the fungo bat at home plate to reach its apex just below the top of the upper deck. The ball was hit to mid left field, far from the wall behind us.

All of a sudden, he ran to his left and then started back. He jerked forward because he realized that the wind was coming from behind him, pushing the ball towards home plate. He stopped quickly and hollered, "Stand right there!"

I stopped thinking. I stopped hearing. I stopped smelling. I stopped doing anything because I looked up and the ball was coming down right where I was standing.

"Put your glove up now!" he yelled. As I did, the ball smacked into my mitt with the sound every pro hears when he makes a catch. It didn't just sting, it hurt more than I could ever imagine. The ball landed right in the mitt's pocket, the area with the least amount of leather. I let out a scream. My hand pulsed with pain so great that I was sure I wouldn't be able to hold a hot dog. I needed ice. Now!

Jungle Jim roared with delight when I looked into my glove and saw the ball. My legs turned to jelly and I felt like I was going to collapse. For a moment, I really had no idea where I was. The sights and sounds of the park went blank. Then, Rivera grabbed me by the arm and started to walk me back to our seats. As we approached the left field foul line, he stopped, looked down at me and smiled. "Think it's easy to be a pro, kid? Welcome to the bigs!"

Uncle Howard met me by the gate with the usher and they escorted me back to my seat. My cousins were there with big smiles on their faces. They knew that this was my once-in-a-lifetime occasion.

The game progressed that day and we ate our way through the nine innings. I don't remember whether the White Sox won or lost, but it really didn't matter. I was a White Sox fan, I was at my first game and I caught a major league ball.

CTA Journal *Sandi Wisenberg*

Red Line, Washington and State

Rush hour you stand on the platform and guys with a cello are singing, "Yoo-oo send me, yoo-oo send me," so that you want to sing along, even move a bit. Harmony. You put a dollar in their box of bills.

At the end of the song no one claps, but the performers aren't nonplussed. (This is different from being plussed.) They say, "Thanks for the standing ovation."

Everyone laughs. The group starts up again. They know that like every captive audience, this one must be won over. They have a specific kind of coyness—for public mass flirtation. The singers hold a note when the southbound comes. When the northbound arrives they say, in a slow, nasal unison: "This train will be running express from Washington to Howard Street." Everybody gets the joke, everybody laughs. In unison.

Most of the audience boards.

22 Clark bus, along Lincoln Park

A couple of guys are talking to everybody—yuppies without much city in them yet, or so much of only one part of the city that, still natty in their suits after 5 PM, they think the whole damn town belongs to them. They start singing and talking to women about drinking, telling jokes. Just about everybody on the bus is just as well-dressed: same colors, creases in the same place. Same tribe.

Possible conversation ploy: Who does your laundry?

Red Line, Jackson and State

Your students are always so amazed, their own personal discovery. It happens in the fall, freshman year. First time away from home. They say: "It's so weird. Did you know that when you wait for the subway downtown, the blacks all go one way and the whites go the other? There's nothing like that in New York"—or Cincinnati or San Francisco or wherever they're from.

Red Line / 22 Clark bus

When he was still living in Lakeview, K. met L. on the bus. They got on at the same time in the morning. She was reading Natalie Goldberg's *Writing Down the Bones*, which he'd thought about buying. They went out for a while. You assume that during their romance they sometimes took the bus together in the morning. Maybe they reenacted the opening scene: "Hello miss, I couldn't help noticing the book you're reading." Or: "Excuse me, ma'am, that's a mighty interesting book you've got there in your handsome little hands." Or: "Darling, I must have you. I've always dreamed of meeting a woman who reads the work of Natalie Goldberg." Oldest line in the book. Now he sees her every once in a while at the gym. He often sees the boyfriend she had after that, the one she doesn't speak to anymore.

Red Line

This was the idea. J.'s friend, the graduate student, liked it. Like a cruise ship. Have everyone on the el who's willing to talk to strangers wear something obvious—a red scarf, for example. Then you would know. Could converse with impunity. While you're commuting. But what if the person who wanted to talk to you wasn't the same person you wanted to talk to?

Red Line

C. tells you she doesn't have her final paper because of what happened the night before. A strange man on the subway told the guy next to her he had to take his seat because C. was his wife. The sitting man complied. The other man started screaming at C. for no reason and grabbed her rough draft and stepped all over it. Finally, someone told him to leave her alone. The conductor did nothing. C. was afraid to get off at her usual stop, scared he would follow her home. She did it anyway.

Red Line, Chicago and State

A Sunday on the platform with B. from Fort Lauderdale, and you see this student coming toward you. She's been waiting for the train so she can drop her paper off at your house.

Brown Line

You like looking at women who look like you, your coloring. Is this so strange? This one has dark wavy hair and a skirt and blouse. Nice clothes, not too tailored, not too boring. Neat. At least not a suit-hose-socks-and-athletic-shoes combo. She's carrying new-looking shopping bags. You try to imagine what's in them. Is she going to go to Crate & Barrel at 8:30 AM to try to return something?

That afternoon, you're at the historic house where you give tours and she walks into the bookstore attached to the house. K., the linguist, is working at the bookstore and asks if you two know each other. The woman remembers meeting you, months before. "I saw you on the el this morning," you say. You find out that in the Crate & Barrel bags were clothes for K. to take. The dark-haired Ravenswood woman lost a lot of weight and has been giving her old clothes to K. to give to a shelter for battered women near her house.

Such satisfaction to know. Like having the answer to a riddle walk smack into your life.

El vs. bus, part one

On the train you often don't see the conductor, so if knowing what the authority figure in charge looks like is a priority, then you are headed for anxiety. On the bus you always know who's driving. On some lines, the drivers know the riders, especially the older women, who walk up slowly, as if on the plank of a ship, sit up close, vigilant. In dreams of community, there are bus drivers like this, who know you, who place you. They are like familiar bartenders or waitresses who smile when they see you and ask, "The usual, babe?"

8 Halsted bus

The driver will stop for you at Halsted and Roscoe and give you a free ride a few blocks to Diversey, where he turns, because you thought this was a bus that went all the way to Fullerton.

If it's cold and nighttime, and you are carrying a bicycle helmet, and the bus is nearly empty, he will ask you the obvious: "Where's your bike?" And you'll say, "About 2600 north," and he'll talk about his bike, and his family, so you'll think: a family man, not trying to pick me up, just being friendly, taking me to my own means of transportation, so that I'll be closer to being able to pedal home on my own power, how nice that everything in the city all fits together.

El vs. bus, part two

While the el gives the illusion of directness, not varying, the bus gives the illusion of freedom; anything is possible because there is no track to get off of, only open road, the apotheosis of middle-class (economic) freedom: let's take a road trip, go places—all is wide open.

29 State bus

On State Street downtown, you decide at the last minute that this northbound bus is as good as any. You tap on the doors just after they close. The driver opens them for you. You ask for a transfer. She frowns: "I don't know if I'll give you a transfer." Can't read this stranger's face. She waits. Her mouth turns to a laugh.

"Oh," you say, "I forgot in your contract you can give them at your discretion."

"Where does it say that?" she asks. "I haven't read it yet. Have you?"

"In the fine print," you say.

This guy in a seat at the front looks at you and says to the driver: "Doesn't she look like a high-powered lawyer?"

You're wearing a striped Indian cotton skirt and blouse and a black vest, sandals, backpack. You think they probably don't dress this way even at the People's Law Office.

He, on the other hand, could fit the part: early 30s, short-cropped reddish beard, dark suit. You get the transfer. Of course. Just playing with you.

But the bus itself betrays you, turns east on Grand, toward Navy Pier. You pull the cord to get off, say good-bye. It's only polite.

Red Line

You can't hear on the subway, but it's easy to forget this if you usually travel alone. But then if you sit next to a friend you end up shouting things like, "He has a pea-brain. I feel like biting him." Looking around furtively, though you know the pea-brain takes another line in another direction.

Even when you're not underground, you find yourself embarrassed when on a crowded night el train, a friend—acquaintance, really—says in a regular voice: "I'll spend two whole days thinking I should be back with her, and then a few days thinking the opposite, is it like that with you, too?"

And you start to answer, then you wave your hands, brushing your proto-confession aside, because—maybe it's just that you're on the el, maybe not—you don't want to inject this damage from the past into this conversation that's moving, moving forward.

Bus / Brown Line

On the bus you can't write—except in big loopy scrawls. It's harder to read, too. Lines wriggle, jolt. But you can look out the windows and remind yourself why you came to the city anyway.

Same with the Brown Line, the view part. You met the aunt of K. while waiting for the Brown Line. The aunt talked to you because you were holding the Louis Sullivan biography. She said she always took the Ravenswood so she could look at buildings.

B., the rosy-cheeked student, late to class one hot spring morning, says: "It was such a pretty day I had to take the Brown Line instead of the Red."

Red Line, Belmont

The prematurely-gray-haired ticket-taker guy seems to know you. You think so by the little flicker in his eye when you say hello or hand him the money.

The newsstand guy always says "Good morning," even though you hardly ever buy a paper from him. Sometimes he burns incense. He looks East Indian, wife, son with him. Sometimes he talks into a powder blue phone. In your maudlin moments you think you are spreading such joy to him with your regular "Good mornings," then you think he probably thinks he's adding a smidgen of warmth to your miserable, solitary life by his regular "Good mornings"; he probably takes joy in thinking how he's making you feel you aren't just some faceless commuter in an endless gray stream of commuters.

Red Line

You are more likely to run into colleagues and exes on the el than the bus. Colleagues are also more likely to run into your exes on the el. Like M., the poet, who came into the office that morning, maybe two days after you and N. had broken up, and, oblivious to it, said, "Oh, guess who I saw on the el." They'd had a light guy-to-guy conversation about leagues and pennants.

R. also ran into N. once on the el. They probably talked about torture (political).

You never run into a current lover on the el or the bus. Or N., either. You've crossed paths twice on North Broadway and twice in Rogers Park. (The worst was when he just got up and left the counter at the Japanese restaurant. The next worst was when you saw him with his girlfriend at the Heartland Cafe and you threw a crumpled-up napkin on their table just to be funny, and missed, and so they saw you just standing behind their table, looking embarrassed. The napkin landed somewhere behind the partition in the smoking section, probably in the middle of some smoker's stir-fried tofu.)

J. ran into your other ex, B., on Clark, or so she thought. He was wearing a jogging suit, like the one he'd worn in your dream. She looked and looked, walked on and then glanced back, not sure if he was indeed B. You've never run into him. Yet. Though you keep seeing men everywhere with similar bald spots. His could have spread by now. The el, the bus, the cafes, bike paths, restaurants, sidewalks, theaters, cars, stores, lobbies, in this town are all filled with balding men.

312-836-7000

Occasionally, you call the information number and they will lie to you about the schedule when you call the free number, but they are always pleasant and the men at least joke with you. Things like: "Yeah, I guess I could tell you when the next bus leaves. What's it worth to you?"

And you think: If I were a foreigner, if my English were weak, I wouldn't know what he was talking about. I would be lost.

212 bus

You can get on or off at any intersection along the way. This is the way of the suburban lines. And the stop-requested pulls always work. But there are never Streetfare Journals to read, only ads to work in the hardware store.

You can leave your poncho on the bus and get off at Davis Street and realize it a few seconds later and go back on and get it. The man sitting in your seat will hand it to you.

Purple Line Evanston Express

You tap him on the shoulder. Haven't seen him in a year or two. Tell him you are looking for a new job. He says to call. You think it's a sign, that a month from now you'll say, "If I hadn't run into him on the el, this never would have happened." But you don't send him the resume. You stay where you are.

Red Line

On the el you can fall in love—like that.

With a profile—something about it, as beautiful as architecture or sculpture. Nice round forehead, perfectly balanced chin. Your reaction is visceral. Like wanting to touch terra-cotta. I must sweep back your straight, straw-colored, poufy-but-not-too hair.

He turns, full face, just before Belmont. Not like sculpture at all. At all.

Call Guinness: the world's shortest self-contained love affair.

36 Broadway bus

On the bus you see parts of the city you haven't seen before because of the angle. On the near-north, on second and third stories: a spa, school of dance, a globe in a window, plants balanced on a row of books, a guy looking over his balcony in front of a sun umbrella, pink shirt, smiling.

Crayon drawings of brown-and-white rabbits in the window of the Cathedral School. It's just past Easter.

A huge sign advertising a lawyer.

The couple behind you says things like: "'Hire me—I'm a hardass.'" "He must be advertising for criminals." "Who else would hire him?"

The city wants to present itself as if from a bus on a sunny Sunday, glass filtering out the smells, showing only what you can see above street level.

Red Line

You were standing on a platform with L., the summer she lived with the Board of Trade runners and knew all the bartenders in town. Sex was on her mind. Two trains arrived from opposite directions at the same time. She said: "Simultaneous. It's really rare." You still think of that. Always. Have stolen her joke. A pretty obvious one anyway.

In transit

You tell your students to write in their journals as often as they can. You have them write down conversations they overhear. Most of them do, but some are self-conscious about it. One of them is berated by a couple whose argument he transcribed. Not M. She's undaunted. Unsinkable. This is what she tells the class: She always writes in her journal on the train. One time she saw that the man next to her was reading her every word. So she wrote: "When the man next to me finishes this sentence he will drop dead."

Our Plan to Save the World
Steve Nelson

We waited until everyone was asleep then we drove all night to Chicago. My mom wouldn't know her van had disappeared until she woke up at seven to get my sis ready for summer school. That first day, I worried about her making it to class on time, but Jenny said, "The world will go on without us." I figured she was right. I would've liked to keep going. Arizona, I guess. Maybe California. But we didn't have the money for gas, and I figured it best to let Jenny do the planning. She was the reason we went. I thought making the decisions might brighten her up. I never would have thought to go without her, but it's true I didn't like it when my mom said, "You're spending too much time with Jenny," or "I don't like the way you look at her." Sometimes she said nothing. When she looked at me, I got the feeling that, at fifteen, I was getting a little too big for her house.

The first few days, Jenny and I stayed close to the van. Moved it from spot to spot. When we were out, we kept walking, trying to blend in. When we saw nobody paid attention to us, or anyone else, we relaxed. We neared the lake and sat on the beach, hiked through the bird sanctuary, looked over the boats in the marina, watched the skateboarders do their tricks. We spent our money on bananas and bread and peanut butter from Aldi, and we pulled the wrapped food out of the dumpsters at the McDonalds or Sonic. Some nights we volunteered at the church on the corner to pass out food. That way, we got to eat too. The first time I said we should just go eat, Jenny said we'd be less suspicious this way. She was right.

Jenny was hotter than blazes for a while, boy, we steamed up that van, though we never got where I thought we might. We joked and teased each other before we left it that *if we ever had some real privacy, we could....*

When we had the chance, it just didn't feel right. Before long, she ran out of her perfume, and we couldn't shower. She started to smell like underarms and french fries, which didn't exactly put me in the mood, so it was no great sacrifice. I knew I was ahead of the game. She took long walks along the lake all the way up to where the big apartments came to the water. She said she wanted to be alone, but I followed behind. At times, I wondered what she was thinking, but mostly I walked and kept her in view.

Some mornings while Jenny slept, I went to the soccer fields to sprint back and forth until I felt like I might pass out. Then I slowly weaved like I was dribbling the ball down field. I hardly ever imagined shooting for goals, because making the good passes was more satisfying for me. I knew soccer season would start soon, and I wouldn't be there. I didn't love it that much, but when I played I forgot about everything else. I'd miss that. Even though I was tired, living like we were, I never got that nice, spent feeling that only came after a long practice or a game—when I felt beat but refreshed. I tried on those mornings, but I never got there.

One day, Jenny said she wanted to go to church. Not to eat, but to go inside and pray. We'd never done this before, and I said I wasn't expecting much but okay. As we walked over, Jenny wouldn't look at me, and she mumbled to herself. I thought she was warming up for how to pray and what to ask for. It didn't matter though because we heard gunshots coming from the church when we were a block away, then saw a car come speeding past us. Figuring it was the shooters, I ducked to hide, but Jenny kept walking. When I caught up to her at the corner, we stood and saw four bodies bleeding and groaning on the church steps. We could smell the powder from the guns. It took a couple minutes for the sirens to follow. We'd seen guys around the neighborhood before who looked like they might be in gangs, but we had never seen any guns or shooting. We turned around and walked back to the van. We tried talking about it a few times, but never got anywhere.

On the weekends big Mexican families grilled in the park and played terrible volleyball games on saggy nets in the dirt. They didn't care they were bad, and they were happy to just be out there. We took in all the smells from the barbeques, saw the meats smoking on the grills, and heard the sounds of the pop cans opening. It was kind of a mix between torture and satisfaction. Torture when we walked through, but afterwards, it was almost like, "Hey, that was pretty good."

Jenny spent some afternoons sitting under trees while she scribbled down poems that she wouldn't let me read. Then we went to the marina, and she threw them in the water. She smiled, so I didn't care. A few nights it got so hot we took a blanket and slept out in the hollows of the golf course. It was nice to wake up with the cool dewy grass, to see the sun coming up, and to hear the birds.

They found us after about a month. A guy walked past our van. He was headed towards Starbucks and recognized us from the news. I read in the paper afterwards that he had seen the Michigan plates, and that Jenny's parents and my mom had been on the news asking about us. I hadn't figured they would go on television, because they wouldn't have known where we were. We could've been in Canada, Cleveland, or anywhere a tank of gas and a couple hundred bucks could get us. But I didn't mind. The police in Chicago were nice enough, and they gave us pizza and Cokes. I knew we couldn't be in too much trouble, because we were both under sixteen and hadn't hurt anybody. I asked them about the shooting at the church, but they wouldn't tell me except to say no one had died.

The police from Michigan picked us up, and Jenny and I got to sit together in the back seat all the way home. My mom hugged me, and I told her I was sorry if she was scared. She said she was but knew I'd be okay. Jenny's parents were crying when we got there. They seemed like tears of joy. Her dad came over to me, and he looked like he was going to give me a friendly handshake. He squeezed it with all his might and whispered, "You're going to pay for this." And then he backed off and smiled at me again when everyone could see. I didn't care. Like I said, it was all Jenny's idea in the first place. Actually, it was her second idea. The first one was to kill herself, and when I told her it was no good, she said, "Well maybe we could just run away." And so that's what we did.

The Coffee Shop   *Joe Mallon*

"You don't mind if I sit here, do you? This place is packed."

Michael looked up. "No problem." He went back to his writing.

The stranger took a sip of his coffee. It was in a mug, not a paper cup, the way everyone else in the coffee shop had theirs.

"You a writer?"

Michael's eyes peered up. "What? Oh. Yeah. A writer."

"Wow. Cool. I could never do that. Can't write a sentence to save my soul." He laughed. The stranger took another sip, looking around the shop. "Man, the line is almost out the door."

Michael ignored him, keeping pen to paper. The guy was annoying. That was the risk of writing in coffee shops. But better than writing at home. Too boring. Too quiet and lonely. He looked down at his cup and winced. Half full and cold. Shit, he thought.

"What do you write?"

Michael looked up. "What?"

"Novels? Short stories? Are you a reporter or something?"

"Novels, mostly. Murder mysteries."

The guy nodded. "Wow. Cool. Death and that. Can't beat a good murder mystery, that's what I always say."

Michael shrugged. "It's a living."

"I mean, who wants to die, right?"

"Everybody dies."

The stranger leaned over. "Yes, but when?"

Michael looked up. "How the hell would I know? When it's your time to go, I guess."

The stranger leaned back in his chair, thinking. "Would you want to know?" he said.

"Know what?"

"The exact time when you were going to die. Down to the minute, the second. Would you want to know?"

Michael resumed writing, ignoring the question. Maybe he'd go away.

"How about this? Would you want to know *where* you were going to die?"

Michael continued to write. But the question took hold of him. Would he? Would he want to know? So he could avoid the place for the rest of his life? He shook the notion out of his head. It was a stupid question.

"Well?" the stranger said.

"Peoria, okay?" He slammed his pen down. "Look, I'm trying to write. Go sit somewhere else or I'll call the barista."

The stranger nodded. "Sorry." He put his finger up to his pursed lips. "Peoria. Interesting choice." He paused. "I wonder if driving through it counts. Or do you have to stop? Say, have a meal or stay overnight on your way to New Orleans or someplace."

"Oh, Jesus Christ."

"Like for Mardi Gras."

"Mardi Gras? I'm driving to Mardi Gras?"

"I'm just sayin'. I mean, it's something to think about, right? I mean, you choose Peoria, you think you're safe. Small town and all that. And all you're doing is driving on I-55 through Peoria, no stops, then BAM! A car crosses the lane, head-on crash, you're dead. Makes you think, huh?"

"No. No, it doesn't." Michael signaled for the barista.

"That ever work?"

"What?"

"Calling for the barista. Tried it myself a couple times. Couldn't get the time of day."

"Of course, I have." Now that he thought of it, he'd never called for a barista before.

"Huh. You must have the Midas Touch." The stranger paused. "Or what if you knew *who* was going to cause your death? Okay. Now that means you gotta take diseases out of it. No cancer, heart disease, nothing like that. I mean, how does a person cause cancer, am I right? No, it has to be some kind of accidental death. Like that driver coming into the other lane." He leaned forward. "Or murder."

"Sir?" Michael raised his hand, signaling again to the barista.

"For instance, what if your fate rested in the hands of a barista? Maybe that one. The one you're trying to call over here. Maybe he's so pissed off— maybe at the job, or at you, or maybe he's just a psych job— he comes over and guts you with a jackknife?" The stranger shivered. "Geez. Wouldn't you want to know if he was the guy?" The stranger stared at Michael. "You could sneak out the back door right now."

The barista still did not respond.

Michael held the stranger's stare for the briefest of moments. "You know what? Keep the table. I'm moving." He packed up, at the same time looking for another table. Nothing.

The stranger looked around as well. "Looks like you're out of luck, buddy. You're stuck with me." He raised the coffee to his lips, this time taking a hard chug. "I got it in a mug. They'll give it to you if you ask, did you know that? Keeps the coffee nice and hot. Tastes better, too."

Michael pulled out his writing materials. He didn't know why he bothered. The morning was wasted by this moron. He slammed his writing tablet down onto the table.

"Look. I really have to get something done."

The stranger held his hands up in surrender. "Okay, okay. I just like meeting new people. I'll be quiet."

The stranger's silence didn't last long.

His voiced lowered. "What if it was me?"

Michael looked up.

"What?"

He smiled. "I said, what if I'm the guy?"

Michael shifted in his seat. He looked around the coffee shop. "What *guy?*"

"You know." The stranger winked. "I mean, what if you pissed someone off bad. I mean really bad. And they wanted it taken care of? In a coffee shop? Say, this one? At," he looked at his watch, then looked up smiling. "One o'clock and thirty-five seconds." He laughed. "And the guy to do it was supposed to be me? Weird, huh?"

Michael glanced at his watch. 12:50. He shifted in his seat again.

The stranger paused, staring at the table, lost in concentration. He slapped the table. "Hey, you know what? This is a great idea for a book, don't you think? Wow! It's like that old film noir movie." He snapped his fingers a couple times, looking at the ceiling. "Now what the hell was the name of it?"

"This is bullshit." Michael stood to go.

The stranger laughed. "Ahh. I'm just yanking your chain," he said, laughing. "Look, I'm going to buy a paper so I don't disturb you. Let me buy you a cup of coffee for the trouble. In a mug. You're going to love it. Stays hot. No paper-taste."

Michael sat back down. Again. He could live with it if the guy read the paper. And he could use another coffee. He stared at the stranger. "Alright. Dark roast. Easy cream, no sugar. And please. You gotta let me work."

The stranger smiled. "Deal. I'm dead to the world once I start reading the Sports section."

The stranger stood up and got in line.

This was shit. He should leave. Find another coffee shop. Or go home, write in his study or at the kitchen table. Hell, writing with his notepad on the Michigan Avenue sidewalk would be more productive. So why did he stay? Something about the guy…

The stranger ordered two cups. He had to admit it. Getting it in a mug was a good idea. The stranger moved over to the cream and sugar table.

Michael tapped his fingers, studying the stranger as the man added cream to both mugs. He returned, placing each mug in front of them.

"Takes a helluva long time to put cream into a couple cups of coffee these days," Michael said.

The stranger smiled. "Cheers," he said, raising his mug.

They touched mugs and both took a sip. The stranger looked at Michael with a look of expectation. "Well? What do you think?"

Michael nodded. "I gotta say. Pretty good."

"Hints of chocolate. Taste it?" The stranger leaned forward.

Michael took another sip. "Yeah, I taste it. Chocolate. Wow. Nice."

The stranger nodded, happy with himself. "Like it, eh?"

"It's good. Gotta admit it. There's another flavor. Can't put my finger on it." He coughed.

"I figure one o'clock. Maybe a little after. I could be wrong."

Michael coughed again. "What do you mean?"

"It's got a nice nutty flavor to it, doesn't it?"

Michael took another taste. He nodded. "Yeah. That's it. It's the chocolate and nutty flavor combined." His breath caught. Why did it feel different? His breathing was odd, strange, difficult.

The stranger crossed his hands. "You remember a girl named Karen? I think you dated her. Then cheated on her. You cleaned out her bank account. Ran up her credit cards. Remember her?"

"My throat." He inhaled, gasping for air. Karen. God, no.

"Me?" He shook his head. "I wouldn't... do something like that... My..." He inhaled. A guttural noise accompanied it. "Karen?"

"She's dead." The stranger stared at him.

Michael's throat closed, his face crimson. Beads of sweat arose on his forehead. "Dead?" His heartbeat grew faster.

"She killed herself. Good kid, from what I hear. But, hey, it happens, right?" The stranger smiled. The smile held a cold hunger.

"It wasn't..." Michael grabbed his throat. "Please," his voice a coarse whisper. The sweat dripped down his forehead.

"Peanuts. You've got a problem with peanuts, am I right? Ironic, because peanuts aren't really nuts."

He pointed at his bag. A gurgle. "EpiPen."

"Sorry, champ, that will be coming with me." He reached inside Michael's bag, removing the EpiPen. "By the way, in case you're interested? Future reference and all? The nuts used in coffee tend to be almonds. I brought my own peanuts. Ground up, of course."

Michael tried to call for help. Nothing came out. He tried to stand, almost knocking over the table. His breath caught inside him. *Gotta call for help.* No words came out.

The stranger smiled, straightening the table. He looked around the crowded coffee shop, shaking his head. "Kids. Look at them." He bent over and dabbed Michael's spilled coffee with a napkin. He leaned towards Michael, whispering, "All they do is look at their phones, listen to their music. Can't hear a thing, don't see a thing. What ever happened to a good conversation?"

Michael tried to motion for the Barista. Again. The stranger held Michaels's arms, like an old friend, and propped him up.

"Easy, champ." The stranger looked at his watch, held it up, and tapped its face. "Wow! Look at the time. 12:58. I gotta blow."

"Please." His voice. Dry. An unwanted whisper. "I'll die."

The stranger wiped his prints from both cups. "Probably at one o'clock and thirty-five seconds. Ironic, eh?"

"Please."

The stranger stood to walk out. He smiled.

"Hey, listen. Good luck with the book."

Lawndale Lyric   *Rose Maria Woodson*

Every year, men came to paint the bottom half of the trees white. All up and down my little block of Spaulding. Was it spring or summer when they came? Can't remember. It was warm, though. I remember that. None of us were wearing coats. It was like we were in some strange little fairy tale. The big, old trees (and yes, they were big and old, with massive crowns of leaves) would watch us go inside, go to sleep. Still plain, they'd rise up to the stars, whispering whatever trees and stars share in whispers. The next day, after school, we'd notice: all the trees wore these painted white tutus. From their waist to their roots. Their bark had been painted over. They were suddenly new, noticed, even pretty. They lined up like ballerinas, poised in a state of grace, waiting for the dance to begin.

And so it was in Lawndale. We were all poised, in a state of grace. In the grace of a community where, as Jane Jacobs would say, there were "eyes on the street."

So many eyes on the street. Ours was a block of three-story homes, a few one-story bungalows scattered between. And of course, a vacant lot. Everybody knew everybody else. Big Momma, yes, Big Momma was almost to the corner of 13th. She was always in the window. Nothing escaped her. We didn't have texting back then. We had Big Momma. And a whole network of grownups. And a network of kids. The Johnson girls lived across the street, down a ways from us. The Payne girls lived in the big three story closer to 13th. And the Woodson girls lived in the middle of the block. Next to us, on one side, was Ms. Kitchen. She was a minister and just the sweetest lady. After we'd grown up, moved away, my baby sister Barbara and I went back to visit her. I wasn't prepared for the Garden of Eden I found after climbing three flights of stairs. Now everybody knew Ms. Kitchen loved plants. When we were kids, we could look up at her porch and see a sea of greenery spilling into the sun. But inside her apartment, we found plants from the front to the back. If there was space, there was a plant. It was a vibrant, beautiful oasis of all kinds of plants, full, with shiny leaves reaching out to you, like angels. On the other side of Ms. Kitchen were two widows, Ms. Davis, in one bungalow and Ms. Murdock next to her. Ms. Lilly, my grandmother's dearest friend, lived on the 3rd floor of our building. And yes, it should have been Mrs. Lilly (she was married to Reverend), but there was something about that extra syllable that made it too proper. So, every woman was Miz. That showed respect without being too fancy, without sounding like an insurance man or a cop.

We had a dry cleaners just across the alley, going towards Roosevelt Road. It was owned by a nice, older black man, Mr. Weathers. There was a corner store, across the street, at 13th and Spaulding, run by Tillie and her husband. In my block, 1200 S. Spaulding, was another little store front. We'd go there for milk, candy, even though Tillie's was the favorite. If we walked down to Roosevelt, turned right, crossing Sawyer, we'd come to Kedzie. Across the street was a big store, Grocerland. It was owned by a couple of Greek men. They were always nice to us. As I grew up, became a "big girl," I'd get to go to the store by myself. I clutched my dollar bills in a brown fist I hoped no one would notice. I remember an older black lady I encountered in the aisle at Grocerland one day, standing in front of Campbell's soup. She asked me to pick out some tomato soup. I found what she wanted, handed the cans to her. She thanked me and walked away. It slowly dawned on me: she couldn't read.

But the stores weren't the only way to get produce. Every day, a white man set up his fruit and vegetable truck right at the corner of Roosevelt and Spaulding. Apples, greens, onions, whatever was in season was for sale. Every day. In the summertime, the watermelon man would drive his truck slowly down the street, calling, "Wat-ter-mel-on! Wat-ter-mel-on!" And people would come out of their houses like a slow hymn. He'd pull over so they could pick out which watermelons they wanted. Sometimes there'd be a little triangle cut out to show how ripe and sweet it was on the inside. Other days, a little white man, we called him the pepper man, would walk slowly down the block, selling his peppers and what not.

I was in graduate school, studying Community Development, when

I first heard the term, "food desert." I'd grown up on the west side, three stores within walking distance, fruit and vegetable vendors a fixture in our neighborhood. Thankfully, food deserts were not part of my childhood.

We didn't just have stores. We had a fish market. All you had to do was walk down to Kedzie, turn the corner towards 13th, and voila! The fish market. It was a big place, sawdust, blood and guts on the floor, men in sloppy, bloody aprons behind the glass cases full of all kinds of fish, scales still shiny, all dead and stretched out on ice, mouths open in a woebegone "o." That was when I knew the difference between split and stake, types of cut you could ask the butcher for. My grandmother was always very specific about which one she wanted. And she always wanted the same cut. I remember my grandparents always had fish on Fridays, even though they weren't catholic. Then they had silver bass. That was served whole. My grandmother baked it to perfection in the oven. Spaghetti on the side.

That place was always busy. In the back, there was a huge tank with the biggest turtle, maybe a tortoise, I'd ever seen. I'd go back there and just watch him swim. Everybody did. Then I'd go collect my fish and head home.

Roosevelt Road was something to behold then. Turn left, now you're walking towards Homan and you have The Rose Shop, a 5 & 10, a drug store. There was a nice white pharmacist there. Maybe he owned the store. I remember you could buy those round glass ornaments there, the ones that came 9 to a square box. Once upon a time, women wore stockings. The Rose Shop carried all kinds of stockings, in colors like Cinnamon and Taupe. My grandmother would send me up there to buy a pair for her. If she had enough money, I'd buy the whole box. The stockings came in a plain, thin, perfectly square white box, with a bit of tissue paper inside. I yearned for the day I'd be old enough to wear stockings. They also had the prettiest handkerchiefs, embroidered in the corner with a fancy flower, some pretty borders. Next to the Rose Shop, I think, was the 5 & 10. They had the best hot dogs in there. If you went the other way, walking down towards Sawyer, there was a clothing store with some really pretty dresses and sweaters. Then you came to the shoe store. All on Roosevelt Road.

If you went down 13th, almost to Homan, you'd find the Douglas Branch Library. It was huge. When you walked in, the children's section was on the right, the adult section on the left. In the summertime, there'd be a Summer Reading Club for kids. You'd read so many books and get a certificate. Mrs. Ballinger was in charge, a sweet lady. I loved getting my certificates. One day, on my own, I made a discovery: I could walk over to the adult side. Nobody stopped me. Nobody called my name. I just walked over, my kid heart both pounding and curious. I think *Podkayne of Mars* by Robert Heinlein was the first book I checked out from the grown-up side.

Across the street from the Douglas Branch Library, on the corner of 13th and Homan, was my elementary school, Lawson. It was a stately building, with a playground. I think it was named for Victor F. Lawson, a white newspaper publisher. I'm pretty sure all of our schools were named for white people: Hess Upper Grade Center, Lathrop Elementary, and Harrison High School. Black kids were both visible and invisible then. The powers that be saw us but never cared to see us.

Still, we had our own state of grace. We had recess. Outside. We didn't get shot. We walked to school. We didn't get shot. We came home for lunch. My grandmother would have homemade lemonade waiting for us, make us bologna or cheese sandwiches. Then we'd walk back to school. We didn't get shot. It seems that the gangs back then had better intel, better aim. They went after each other, knew where to find each other. Didn't shoot into cars, crowds, houses.

It was a different time. When kids had fights, after school, it was mano a mano. A circle of onlookers would form, shouting taunts, egging them on. Fists would fly. If girls were fighting, add hair pulling to flying fists. Maybe a few forbidden cuss words thrown in. Then, it'd be over. I could count on one hand the number of fights I had in grade school. Which is fortunate since my mode of defense was the windmill: whipping my arms round and round in the hopes of keeping my opponent too far away to land a punch. I was a thinker, not a fighter.

If you went the other way on 13th down to Sawyer, you'd find the Greater Open Door Baptist Church. It was a big, beautiful church, not a storefront. It must have been a synagogue before, because on the ends of the pews was the a six-pointed star. After I went to college, I found out the six-pointed star was the Star of David. As a kid, I just saw a star. We went to church and Sunday school. When you walked in, the older kids had Sunday school in the back, to your right. Little kids were upstairs. My Sunday School teacher was Ms. Patterson, a sweet, brown skinned lady who wore glasses. I remember her saying one time that we had to have rainy days so we'd appreciate the sunny days. Sadly, later she went blind. Upstairs, Mrs. Richardson was in charge of the toddlers. After I got older, I worked up there. We went to church on Sundays, BTU, bible study on Wednesdays. Every summer, we'd go to vacation bible school for two weeks. All kinds of fun activities. But it was in the Baptist church that I learned just how slowly time churned. Clean shaven men would emerge after Sunday sermon with full beards. Still, I have fond memories of that church, the fellowship and friendships. I can still hear Mr. Lamar, the Sunday school superintendent, saying, "Please, ma'am and please, sir," before any especially important announcement. I can still see the sea of red and white carnations and other flowers among the congregation every Mother's Day. You wore red if your mom was still alive, white if she had passed. People would actually stand on sidewalks before Mother's Day, with their board of red and white flowers, some small, just a bud, others more ornate, elaborate corsages complete with ribbons and baby's breath.

We had a sweet childhood. We'd come home from school, do our homework, watch *Wonder Woman* on TV. We loved that show. Mom would do the Wonder Woman spin. For years. And rightfully so, as I think back now: she was our Wonder Woman. She made good things happen for her four brown girls. On our birthdays, she'd bring a sheet cake up to the school. "Happy Birthday, Rose" "Happy Birthday, Barbara" "Happy Birthday, Debbie and Valerie" inscribed across the icing. We'd celebrate with our classmates. Everybody was included. She taught me how to read before I went to school. We always had books in our home, hardcover classics: *Black Beauty, Treasure Island.* I remember Mom and I sitting on the bed, writing a poem together. I always say I've been writing since I was five years old. That poem. She poured poetry into our young lives in her own unique way. We knew it was officially summer when she took us on the Wendella boat ride. I remember my mom taking us on the Roosevelt bus. We'd always get a seat. Ride to the end of the line. The bus would turn around. We'd ride back. How the neighborhoods would change the further east we went. That was my mom's way of broadening our horizons.

At Christmas time, Mom and the four of us would stand on the front porch and sing Christmas carols to the neighborhood. We did that more than once. I just remember standing up there, serenading the world with joy. These were special times for me for another reason. I can't sing. My voice, a train wreck on its own, could easily get lost in the choir of mother and sisters. I've asked my mom repeatedly where she got me: my mother has a beautiful voice, all of my sisters could sing (they joined choir, I joined band). My grandmother was a wonderful soprano. I just know I must be a family secret: a foundling. Where did she find me? In a grocery cart? Somebody tucked me in between broccoli and Hi C? On a bus seat? Maybe she'll tell me one day.

We had a good life in Lawndale. A full life. Not a perfect life. The powers that be were in play even then. Even now, my mother remembers white detectives, white police setting upon black men as they walked home from church with their families. In front of their wives and children, throwing them up against buildings or down to the ground. For nothing. Once, one of my mom's former patients, a sweet Greek lady, Stella, came to one of our birthday parties at home. She'd taken a cab there and before she got out, the white cab driver asked her if she was sure this was where she wanted to go. Later, white police intruded on our celebration, saying they'd had a tip drugs were being sold there. All they found was a room full of bewildered black kids, my mom, my play aunt Stella and cake and ice cream. We always figured the white driver phoned the cops.

We had our own neighborhood bad guys. There were a couple of brothers. Imagine two portly, brown skin versions of Eddie Haskell. I will not name them. They may still be floating around in the universe. They were unctuous to the nth degree. "How you doin', Miz Woodson? You girls, how you doin'? How's school? Y'all some smart little girls. Miz Woodson, you just a great lady, a real good mom. We'll be seein' y'all." And so on. It was rumored, and I believe it, these brothers knew how to cut the street lights off for the whole block. Lord help you if you ran in to them that dark night, your paycheck just cashed. Bad dudes. Their sister, on the other hand, was so nice. She became a preacher.

I'm sure the experts labeled us poor. If we were poor, we were working class poor. Most of the men and women worked. I'd see them leaving for their jobs when I was leaving for school. I talked to the other kids. Sometimes they'd talk about their dad's job, where their mother worked. My own mom was a nurse. When my mom divorced my father, my father divorced his daughters. So, it wasn't unusual for Mom to work double duty: 7 to 3, 3 to 11. She did private duty for a while, then worked at Mary Thompson Hospital and finally at Franklin Boulevard Hospital (which later became Sacred Heart). We were never hungry. We had new spring coats and dresses for Easter. New clothes every fall for the start of school. My grandfather was a cook at a veterans' hospital. He made wonderful chili, dressing for Thanksgiving. We were never latchkey kids: my grandmother quit her job at the cleaners to take care of us. She made me laugh telling me how she tried everything to get fired, because she wanted to babysit us. Finally, she just had to quit. The best laid plans of mice and grandmothers.

Back then we had our church, our schools, our stores. We even had Sears, just down on Arthington. But the presence of Sears went beyond the function of a major, full-service department store. Sears gave us a garden: a beautiful, sunken garden. It was a rectangle of heaven, blooming, vibrant, unexpected. I remember my grandmother and I walking over one day just to see the flowers, those gorgeous blossoms, a rainbow of red, pink, yellow, lilac petals. It was intoxicating.

We had a community. We had roots. We had the mecca of Roosevelt Road.

The day Martin Luther King was assassinated, all that changed in the smoky blink of an eye. Everybody was outside, worrying, milling around, looking down at the flames roaring on Roosevelt. It was a war zone. All hot, searing hurt raging, rising into the night. I remember my mom saying, "If the fire jumps the alley, we have to go." And I thought then, as I think now, go where? We were a small family. There were no cousins, aunts or uncles in Chicago. And even if there were, how could we get there? There was no safety in the streets. Buildings burned. Looters took advantage. If the fire had jumped the alley, the only thing we could have done was cry. We thanked God the fire did not jump the alley. We cried anyway. Martin Luther King was dead. Roosevelt Road was dead, crashing from bustling to rubble. It stayed rubble for many, many years. Glass, broken as black hearts, littered sidewalks, mixed with ash and smoldering frames. All the people who worked in all those stores lost their jobs. Overnight. We lost our mecca. Overnight. A ghost town suddenly appeared in the aftermath of mad sadness.

Bones of burned buildings are sirens. They call to you, haunt your dreams. Hover in your waking. They tell you it's the end of the world. You are still as trees, rooted under starless night, rooted in what was. Choked. Broken. Chained in ash and smoke. In darkness, you move toward a light not yet seen. It is not the end of the world. But it is the end of *a* world.

The Hierarchy of Grief
Dipika Mukherjee

For the past two years, Dr. Nash has been prescribing sedatives and antidepressants. It must be the medication slowing my heart down so that I can't climb any stairs. And the breathlessness that wakes me up at nights, gasping for air and finding none.

I am alone on such nights. My wandering irritates no one; there is nobody to be disturbed by the sound of the TV at three in the morning, when insomniacs are peddled things they don't need. There is no child to climb sleepily on my lap, such weighty love.

Dr. Nash has shepherded me through the past years; she knows how fragile I have become, I, once undaunted by life. I once thought the universe modulated its flow to make my life easier, to make the desires of Aneesh and Anwesa come true because of the merits of past lives and daily prayer.

Then the Malaysia Airlines flight disappeared, like a star extinguished in the night sky, taking Aneesh and Anwesa from me. I flew to Kuala Lumpur earlier than I was expected.

When Kyra hooked me up to the ECG machine at Dr. Nash's office this morning, her hands were clumsy. She is young, interning while waiting for medical school acceptances, and very apologetic. She peeled the monitors off my skin again and again. When the sheets were printed out and Dr. Nash told her to wheel me into the emergency room at Northwestern Medical, she stumbled near the elevator, pitching me forward. My blood pressure registered 181/120. They did another ECG at the emergency room and mumbled about T-wave abnormality.

Kyra asked whether someone could be with me, and when I said no, she didn't press further. She bought me lunch from Saigon Sisters upstairs (thoughtfully Asian and only slightly spicy), and I ate on a gurney in the emergency room. Kyra looked defeated when she left.

Now I am in the cardiac care unit, a place filled with old men my father's age. I think of my father, so far away, seated in front of the TV, windows open to the tropical heat and pollution of Damansara Utama because he can't bear air-conditioned rooms. It is early morning in Malaysia; my mother is reading the papers over her morning tea.

There is a cry from a room opposite, then sobbing, then it all goes quiet.

I know now to interpret signals of grief. Sobbing does not come to everyone, such easy relief.

I am watching the screen; a human heart in action. It is a beautiful thing, this pulsating pumping masculine organ within my female body, creating lines that squiggle into mountains and hills with flat lands in between. I hold my breath, wondering if it will change slightly. It doesn't, this mechanical thing. The black lines on the page continue a traitorous path.

Anwesa is a writer. She talks of black lines on a page and their ability to transport minds like magic. She is learning to read and write Bengali now, and delighting in curlicues of the script in her mother tongue. Aneesh and I tease her about being an American Born confused Malaysian finding Bengali roots in college, but we are secretly thrilled that Anwesa is a freshman at University of Chicago, and still so close to home.

Was close to home.

Ina, the technician, shifts slightly, allowing cool gel to probe the underside of my right breast, and a long tongue, flapping as if torn, appears on the screen.

"Is there a problem?"

Ina is measuring cavities and edges with precise red cross marks. "That's a valve that blocks the regurgitation of blood. Perfectly normal."

"Would you tell me if you saw something abnormal?"

She smiles. Her eyes are kind, used to dealing with frightened patients who find themselves in this room without much notice, but then again, maybe she knows. "The doctor will read these images and speak to you later. Let me put it this way… if I see something concerning, you won't get on that treadmill."

"So if I take the stress test, my heart is fine?"

"I can't tell you that." She carries on probing.

The radiologist is a blond Midwesterner who probably wants to be out on the streets, just like Ina, ushering in another New Year, with its promise of new beginnings. Instead they focus on the pulsating screen.

How did my heart keep on pumping through the months when it seemed so much easier to just give up? I willed it to give up, for my body to also become a non-corporeal thing, spiraling towards Aneesh and Anwesa in a galaxy of stars. *To cease upon the midnight with no pain.* A young English poet, I forget who, had written those lines, and died an early death. Anwesa had driven me crazy memorizing that poem for a slam event, juxtaposing the macabre lines with a modern poem on police brutality on black bodies. She had performed this at the Printers Row Literary Festival; on that bright summer day filled with young families buying books from makeshift stalls, that performance left the audience bewildered.

I now understand the conceit of singing in a dark garden, the happiness of death. I once stopped taking the medication that regulated this body, controlled my hypertension, until I had collapsed, needing to be whisked into Northwestern Memorial's Emergency Room in an ambulance that shrieked past the holiday crowds thronging Michigan Avenue, and into a room of people asking me whether I knew which year it was, who the President of the United States was, and which city I was in.

I am becoming old friends with Northwestern Medical, but the only room I really want to be in is the morgue.

I have seen therapists. I have mourned with Aneesh's family and mine in Malaysia for thirteen days, loud bhajans every evening, the community coming together as a protective comforter around me for the two months I stayed. I followed the rituals, even taking imaginary cremated bones to the Malacca Straits on a boat and setting the flowers-that-were-their-ashes free. I eat nothing made out of any cereal at ekadashi, no onion, no garlic, no meat.

Nothing helps.

No one warns you that grieving is a game of one up-manship. In

121

Malaysia, women who had been widowed, parents who had lost children, even women who had miscarried... they all came to tell me they understood my grief. An Aunt told me about a neighbor who lost both her sons in a car crash, as if losing one child was easier than losing two, as if death was a hierarchy of grief. I grew tired of the How Are Yous? when no one understood how I tottered from moment to moment, veering between disbelief and hope.

So I came back, to Chicago, which has been home for the past four years but where we are still strangers. In this big city, I can go for days without talking about Aneesh or Anwesa, teaching my students, then returning to the closet where I sleep surrounded by Anwesa's fragrance. Sometimes I sleep on Aneesh's shirts, the ones casually discarded in the laundry basket.

Dr. Nash wants me to not read the news reports or watch TV anymore, at least until I am stronger. So I don't. But this morning, on the purple line to Evanston, the man across from me was reading the *Chicago Tribune* and there was a picture of a little boy, like a doll, washed up on the shoreline.

My heart started to pound. I thought of the parents of this child, prayed that they were washed up on some shore like this, instead of bearing the worst curse of humanity. I got off at Dempster. I sat in the train station for an hour, but my heart would not subside.

I know the drill by now. Ina asks me to get on the treadmill, run until I can't run anymore, and then quickly slide onto my right side on the examination table before my heart has a chance to slow down. I have my running shoes on.

"Good job," she says. "This isn't very comfortable, I know, but you're doing great."

She knots the hospital gown over my chest as a male technician walks in to look at the screen.

He nods.

"Can I go home now?"

"Probably," she says cheerfully. "We'll have to wait for the doctor."

They will not find anything wrong with me. The midnight MRI, the stress tests and EKG... all will be clear. No Evidence of Ischemia, No Arrhythmias, Normal Resting BP with Appropriate Response to Exercise. I have done this too many times. Random pictures— a dead child, a plane in the air— sets my heart palpitating and sometimes that forces me into Dr. Nash's office, then the hospital.

I imagine Anwesa in the firmament, her hand clasped in Aneesh's, and I know he will never let her go. If one of us has to be with Anwesa like this, Aneesh is the intrepid parent, her doting dad. But usually, this image is followed by Anwesa plummeting to earth with terror in her eyes.

Maybe there *is* a hierarchy of grief. I mourn for Anwesa in a way I don't for Aneesh. Perhaps we both mourn for the child we birthed, but only one of us has been sentenced to a life of cruel and unusual grieving.

The nurse wheels me back to my room, where the TV is on. The dead Syrian child has a name now and the talking heads are debating on why the Middle East isn't taking in any refugees, whether Europe can accept the burden of more; one man calls the parents selfish for putting a child on a boat.

Even if I don't read the news, I know that what is happening in Syria on land is worse than the risks at sea. But why did we, Aneesh and I, take Anwesa away from Malaysia? We didn't put her on a boat, but we too cast ourselves adrift from everything familiar. The Malaysian government was fanning a brand of ethnic politics that had ushered apartheid, especially in education; it was no longer a place for bright young non-Malay people like Anwesa. When his multinational company offered to transfer Aneesh to Chicago, we grabbed this opportunity for her.

That is what we told ourselves as Anwesa wrote through an alienated year of high school, grieving for home, as one of the few brown kids in her class. Always searching for something a flight away, Anwesa went to Malaysia for a few weeks in summer every year. We had taken Anwesa out of a failed educational system, a country festering in corruption, but we had also taken away who she was before she could become someone new.

How long does it take to belong in a country?

MH370 is still a mystery. The politics of Malaysia do not make the news in Chicago, for Malaysia is no Syria, torn apart by a civil war or overcome by Islamists. Even the Malaysian anti-government rallies are peaceful. I don't remember much from the first two weeks back in Malaysia after the disappearance of the flight, but I know we were allowed no public rage, herded as we were into newsrooms as pawns and dragged out if our grief became a national shame.

Our children are not washed up on seashores. They have

disappeared, as if they had never lived.

Is there a right path? Sometimes we get to choose our own passing—a slow erosion or a sudden goodbye— in this life. No one should mourn my death. I will leave this earth of borders and nations, soar into a place that has Aneesh and Anwesa waiting, a space large enough to embrace us all.

Afternoon Cartoons   *Marc Baker*

Our grandparents had rabbit ears on their tv, connected, I think, to a bigger one on the roof. Two channels that we didn't get at our house—32 and 44. We would watch cartoons after school, my brother and I.

> *Da denh da denh denh denh*
> *Spider-man Spider-man*
> *does whatever...*and so forth.

He'd hurtle from the couch—my brother—into my arms, and we'd tumble across the floor. He'd pin me if I let him. Then *Speed Racer* and we'd be off, tearing circles into the rug, scaring the cat. Then *The Banana Splits* or *Prince Planet* unless the Sox were on. Then, instead, we'd hear Harry call Big Dick Allen's number 15.

Cartoons were better, but baseball was ok. It was only when cartoons turned into news then into my grandparents' programs that our tumblies grumbled, prompting gramma to bring out cheese sandwiches to tide us over until dad, instead of mom, came to get us. Because she had a headache from her treatment or just "enough of those kids."

People Gotta Eat *Paul Teodo & Tom Myers*

Steam drifted lazily, circling the enormous white serving bowl; the story behind each chip and crack handed down with the platter from nonna to nonna. A box and a half of spaghetti, nestled in the family relic, was now covered in red sauce under neck bones. A rusty grater, balanced on its side, waited with sharp claws to shred a pungent wedge of Asiago.

His mother, the straps of her blue flowered apron tied over her shoulders, looked antsy, as if a word in her mouth was trapped like a caged sparrow waiting to escape. His father, a powerful eater, face down in his plate, attacked the meal like a man just returned from battle: a piece of crusty bread in one hand, his favorite fork in the other. His sister, 11 and worldlier than him, hummed something from the radio to herself.

The boy was just 8 but could tell this was different.

His mother cleared her throat.

He knew it. *What was up? What was she going to say?*

His father, focused on his plate, tore a piece of bread from the loaf and slopped up some gravy. Ten hours in the factory made him like that. His gastric eruptions could be heard from the bathroom while he changed from his baggy, sweat-stained pants and scrubbed his face and hands with Lava soap, futilely trying to remove the dirt and grime. She cleared her throat again. His sister stopped humming. They were silent, except for his father's fork extracting strands of meat from a neck bone while crunching bread between his powerful jaws.

"I bought a store."

His father stopped mid-scoop, spaghetti and neck bone dripping sauce dangling an inch from his bristly chin. "A what?" Sounding as if the neck bone of the slaughtered pig was now lodged deep in his throat.

"Rose loaned me the money."

126

"Rose?" His father's voice burst through the food, bounced off the walls. He grabbed his wine glass and swallowed hard. "She cuts ladies' hair. What's she know about stores."

"She's successful. And she knows how much I want this."

"You bought a store, and you didn't tell me?"

"Yes," she said, her voice low but confident.

"We talk about things."

"If I had told you, you would've yelled and said no. And I didn't want to waste time arguing. So she loaned me the money."

"What money?" His father's voice commanding, hand slamming his fork down, the cheese grater and the Asiago falling to the floor. Bruno, their ninety-pound alley dog, who'd been lurking in the corner, went for it. The cheese, like a magic trick, vanished, the dog's snake-like tongue slithering over its jowls.

"Three hundred dollars," she said, clear as a bell. "I'll pay her back."

"Rose loaned you the money?"

"I've always wanted to own a store."

"Whatta you gonna do with a store? We're not those kinda people. We *work* for those kinda people."

"I'm gonna sell things," she said, not giving ground.

"Sell what?" His father shot back in the chair, his meal now forgotten. "Whattaya gonna sell?" He stood, not able to contain himself, face crimson, biting his lip, red sauce spotting his white t-shirt.

"Nice things. Holy cards, statues, rosaries, maybe some candles."

"For Chrissake! We got nothing. And you go out and..." His mother's face turned ashen.

His father stopped. He was a yeller. He spoke loud, he yelled louder. It was a yell he'd gotten down good, a staff sergeant in the army. *The war was a bitch*. When she'd ask him to lower his voice he'd say, *When I was scared that voice saved lives. I yelled over the bullets, the bombs, and the crying.*

The war is over, she would reply.

He stood silent, his face softening. Lost.

His mother's sigh filled the room with disappointment. His father remained standing, fork still in hand. Once more he began, but it was a yell. He stopped. His breath heavy and wet. Sweat bloomed the gravy stains on his shirt.

Silence.

His mother looked fragile, alone, wounded.

The little boy's eyes darted between the two of them. *Please God, make it okay.*

His father's love for her burrowed deep. When she looked like this, he knew he'd hurt her. He couldn't stand to see her in pain. Especially if caused by him.

Hands trembling, she found a white lace handkerchief under her apron and dabbed her eyes. She began slowly, "I have a name for…." Trying to catch her breath, she stumbled over her words. After a labored pause, she whispered, "…the store."

"What name?" The little boy could tell Daddy was trying not to yell.

"Enzio's," she said, her voice now soothing, supportive.

"After Daddy!" his sister blurted.

The little boy's head spun towards her. He wanted to shove a napkin in her mouth.

"Yes, after Daddy," his mother said, blotting her tears, a sly smile lighting her face. "Enzio's."

His father shook his head like a dog with something stuck in its ear. "Enzio's," he said, barely audible. "Enzio's," he repeated, as if he hadn't heard it the first time.

"Look," his mother said. She slid a piece of paper from her apron pocket. Unfolding it with great care, as if it held a precious stone, she presented it to him. His father scowled.

The little boy could see an "E", then an "N", then a "Z"… and in bold letters it was all there. **ENZIO'S.**

"Daddy," his sister squealed, "Momma named her store for you!"

"*Her* store?" His father's voice sly with sarcasm.

"Yes. Rose gave her the money. It's *hers.*" His sister never shy about adding to any conversation.

"Rose made the sketch for the sign," she spread the paper on the table. "We'll hang it over the door."

The sketch stared up from the table. His father stared back. "Enzio's" his mother said softly. "I've always wanted a store."

"When are you gonna open?" his father asked, returning to his chair, pushing Bruno's inquisitive nose from the table.

"Next week."

"Next week?" His father shook his head. "Next week?"

"How'd it go?" he asked.

"Wonderful," she said. "Dozens of people came."

"How much did you take in?" His voice like a curious inspector.

"Do you like the roast?"

"It's great. How much did you take in?" Bruno lingered at his side, large snout surveying the scene.

"It's a new recipe. Rose gave it to me."

His father cringed like he'd been jabbed with Grandma's knitting needle.

"Did you sell a lot of statues or holy cards or rosaries?"

"Rose says it takes time."

His father mopped the napkin over his chin and tossed it on the table.

"Rose this! Rose that!" He yelled. "What does she know?" Bruno roared a bark that rustled the curtains. "How much time?"

"Time, just time, you know. Have some more roast."

His sister chimed in. "You should see it, Daddy. The statues are in one spot. Big ones, little ones. The holy cards are so nice. Jesus, Mary, Joseph, all lined up. Even some saints. And Momma has some rosaries too. And the candles, they smell so good."

His father shook his head slowly, his face contorted like a man determined not to cry out while being disemboweled. "Honey," he lowered his voice, struggling to infuse sweetness into his tone, "how much did you sell?"

The little boy wanted to help his mother, who looked as if she was in the pool at the park, in the deep end, just realizing her toes couldn't touch the bottom. "Rose…" she began.

"Rose!" He slammed his hand on the table, a piece of roast dropping to the floor; Bruno, reverting back to the alley, ripped at the meat, gleefully wolfing down the damage Rose, the hairdresser, had caused.

"Why are you like this?" His mother stood.

"What? Like what?" His father ripped the meat from Bruno's mouth.

"Yelling, angry."

Why AM I *like this,* his father thought. *Yelling? Angry?* Because he was scared and ashamed. Like a man who had just pleaded guilty to stealing a loaf of bread, loathing himself for not being able to feed his family without breaking the law.

"I'm sorry," he said, his pain, fear, and sadness no longer hidden by his rage. "I am, so sorry," his voice diminished, humble.

His mother took his father's hand, put it to her lips, kissing the rough gnarled knuckles. She took a deep breath. "Nothing," she said softly. "I sold nothing."

The little boy stood on his toes peering over the weather worn banister framing the second-floor porch of the two-flat. He liked it high up here. It was scary, but he got a good view of the neighborhood. Mr. LaManto's fig tree grew like a stately statue in the middle of his backyard and when it was cold, he'd cover it with a big blanket. Mrs. DiNardo soaked stinky fish in a bucket on her porch, and Freddy Farraro's bathtub, filled with dirt, growing tomatoes, rested on the roof of his rickety old garage. Smells lingered, thick and heavy throughout the air: olive oil, garlic, basil, and onions.

He studied his father sitting on a bucket turned upside down. Stones and pieces of broken glass littered the brown grass scattered in the dry gray dirt. His father looked old, tired. His head down as if a weight pulled his thick neck towards the earth.

Momma's store wasn't doing so good. The women who came in talked and laughed, holding up the cards and examining the statues. But they'd put them back on the shelf and leave with nothing in their hands. He hated it. He lingered behind the counter listening to the endless chatter, ready to make a sale. Momma had trained him with real money, a cigar box under the counter where he was supposed to put the cash. But the box lay empty, day after day.

No boys ever came in, just mothers, sometimes with their little girls, cooing and clucking, admiring a statue, telling a story about a saint, or bowing their heads piously as they fingered a rosary.

He thought of his mitt hung on his bedroom wall stiff from lack of use. As he walked through the park each morning, he longed for the dusty diamond.

The slam of the wooden gate startled him. He stood taller to see who it was. Momma, looking tired, trudged into the barren backyard.

His father looked up. "How was your day?" His voice low, heavy with concern.

"It was good. And yours?" she said, matching his tone.

"Fine. Hot, but fine. I make tape. It pays the bills." He shrugged. "It's just tape."

"It does," his mother said.

"We're running three lines and there's at least two hours overtime whenever I want it. Time and a half. Who can complain?"

"What's this?" She pointed at the bucket.

"Just thinking." His father rose gingerly, stretching.

"About?"

His father did not reply. He watched a bird picking stop-start at strands of straw, chirping wildly, fluffing its nest in the gutter of Mr. LaManto's house. He nodded to the bird, speaking slowly, barely audible. "He's working hard."

"I thought it would be different." Her eyes still fixed on the bird.

The little boy strained to keep his balance, his calves aching.

His father looked at his mother, nodding. "It's not easy," taking her hand in his.

"I don't know what to do," a catch in her throat. "I feel so bad."

He pulled her close. She rested her head on his chest.

She looked up at him. "Will we have to close? Bankrupt?"

He lightly held her shoulders studying her as if trying to figure how to say what he was going to say. "People gotta eat."

"They need to eat?"

"They need to eat. Statues, candles, holy cards. They are..." he paused, "you can't eat them."

"What are you talk—?"

His father placed his crooked finger on her lips. "Aspetta, mi amore, wait," his voice straining. "You cook the best. Your gravy, peppers, the sausage, meatballs, eggplant, nobody can compare. People need food. You make the best."

"You're trying to cheer me up."

"No. It's the truth. People want food. Good food. Yours is the best. I will help."

"With what?"

"Cooking, the store. I can help. You can teach me."

"I wanted the store for...."

"We can keep a place for the statues, rosaries, the cards, candles, all of that, a special shelf. But we must sell food."

"Do you really think...?"

"It's been four weeks. We've sold nothing. The people that come in and look, they talk," he made a little flapping gesture with his hand. "They feel good, but they don't buy. They like the store. They like you, but they leave with nothing. With your store, they'll come in and buy your food." He held her face in his hands. "If we don't do this, we'll lose the store."

"How can I do it? We have kids."

"The kids will be in school. You do the days. I'll do the nights."

"You work."

"I'll work more."

"You can't do that."

His father stepped back slightly. He held her shoulders in his hands. "I want you to be happy. You want this. You deserve it. We can do it. Together. A team. The kids will help. It'll be good for us. A family store."

"Here." His father handed him a big black marker. "This too." He removed a large piece of red construction paper from a bag that lay on the dining room table. "Write this, *salami*."

"I don't know how to spell it," the little boy said.

His father looked around like he'd lost something. "Where's your sister?"

"I don't know."

"Serafina!" His father's voice boomed through the tiny flat. "Serafina!" Again, louder. His sister, still in pink PJ's, stumbled out of her bedroom. "Here." His father pointed to the table covered with red paper. "Sit. You're a good speller. Help your brother."

"I'm tired."

"Spell salami," his father ordered.

"Why?"

"We're making signs to hang, in the building, for the store. All over."

She sat, scanned the table, then rubbed her sleepy eyes. "We need more colors."

"What?" her father yelled, gulping coffee like it was his first cup after Lent.

"You can't make signs with just one color. It's prettier if you have more."

"Prettier!" His father's voice rose. "We don't need..." he paused,

132

inhaling. "Fine, get more," pointing in the air, befuddled, like a man who hoped multicolored paper would magically appear.

She smiled, and with new found enthusiasm, hopped from the table, swung open the lower door of the china cabinet, and yanked out a box overflowing with green, yellow, blue, and orange construction paper.

"Salami," his father said. He sat his daughter down and pointed to the paper, his son poised ready to go to work. "Spell it."

After an hour, a staggering array of colored construction paper, printed with a variety of lopsided advertisements for Italian staples, covered the table. *Salami, Gabagool, Mortadella, Soppressata, Gravy, Sausage, Meatballs, Subs, Melanzane.*

"It's not right." She said, chastising her father.

"Whataya mean?" He snorted.

"That word."

"Which one?"

"Gabagool. That's not what Momma calls it."

"That's how my people say it."

And printed on three pieces of paper taped together, green, white, and red: "Grand Opening. Come Buy at Enzio's and Wife Italian Foods. It's THE BEST!"

"Let's go," he said, grabbing a roll of tape he'd pilfered from work. "Now we hang, in the whole neighborhood."

"Big day." His father hugged his mother. They stood arm-in-arm in the tiny store. His mother wore her blue flowered apron, his father's, blood-spattered on white, draped across his belly.

"Will anyone come?" she asked, head down, smoothing her apron.

"They'll come," his father said as if it were a threat. "You cook good. You'll see."

The tiny bell over the door jingled. A woman with two small children trailing pushed through. She stopped. Closing her eyes, she inhaled. "My god," she said clutching her chest, "what's that smell?"

"What do you want to buy?" his father snarled like she was a buck private.

The woman backed away, protecting her children, as if they were about to be assaulted by a man in a bloody white apron.

"Let me," his mother said. She turned to the woman. "Your children are beautiful. I love that little dress. You must be talking about the sausage and peppers. My mother's recipe."

The woman's face softened. "I'll take some, and do you have any frittatas?"

"Yes, we do." His mother's happy voice lifted into the air.

The bell above the door jingled again, and again, and again. It jingled all day. The steady stream of awkward, not-knowing-what-to-expect customers, carrying red, green, and orange, hand printed signs continued throughout the day.

"What's a Gabagool?" asked a short bald man, holding a sign.

"It's good, you'll like it," his father barked.

"Gimme two pounds of Mor-tee-dalia," another said, raising the sign he held in his hand, his lips contorted as if the dentist had just finished digging around in his mouth.

"I teach you right word," his father responded like a professorial maestro standing before his obedient symphony. "Mortadella." The word rolled off his tongue like lava down Vesuvius.

And "I'll take a dozen meatballs to go," one guy with a huge mustache yelled over the throng.

"A dozen balls, for the mustachio!" His father's voice rose above the crowd.

One after the next, shoulder to shoulder, the store was packed from open till close. Yelling, laughing, and buying. Some even trying to outbid the other on a container of gravy or a tray of lasagna.

The day ended with all the salami, gabagool, sausage, peppers, gravy, meatballs—everything they made— gone. Serafina stood in the center of the store, hands on her hips, announcing, "Like a pack of wild dogs, like Uncle Frank and the cousins were here."

And it was like that for five years. Everything she made flew off the shelves or out of the cooler. Enzio's and Wife Italian Foods was the talk of the neighborhood.

Rose was paid off a week after the Grand Opening, and Momma never looked so happy.

"People need to eat." His father would say as he struggled to make small talk with each customer that entered the store.

And it was good for the family.

The little boy, however, rarely saw his father, who still worked at the tape factory 7 in the morning till 4, Monday through Friday. At 4, his father walked from the factory to the store. On Saturdays and Sundays, the whole family worked there. The little boy's mitt, still hanging on the wall, grew stiffer with disuse.

He, his sister, and his mother walked through the park to the store at 6 every morning to open. At 5 they all ate supper in the back; during the meal, his mother and father took turns waiting on customers. At 6:30, the little boy, his sister, and his mother walked home through the park to their second-floor flat.

His father closed the store at 10, walked home, and collapsed in bed. Five years, every day.

The school bell rang at 3. The little boy was glad to get away from Sister Lilliana, the worst nun ever. He began his daily trek to the store. Momma was there and Serafina would be there soon. His job every day was to throw away the garbage. It was heavy but he could lift it. He'd get the big key and unlock the metal gate that made him feel like he was in jail, then drag the big bags into the alley. It smelled bad, but it was his job.

This time, as he approached the store, it was different, he could tell. He walked in. The bell did not jingle. No greeting, no smile. No Momma. He couldn't breathe. He looked around. He tiptoed towards the back. One foot, then the other. Hands trembling. His stomach felt like he'd been punched.

He saw her feet first. Then her legs. Then her blue flowered apron. She was on the floor, arms crossed as if she was praying. Her lip bleeding, her eye swollen. He kneeled next to her. He tried not to scream. His insides exploding, he crossed himself. He prayed.

They'd been robbed. Momma was taken to the hospital. The doctors asked her questions. She said she was fine. She came home, moving slowly. Daddy and Momma talked in the bedroom. Their voices muffled, then rising, then lower.

Two days later, Daddy announced the store would close. His eyes were wild but filled with tears. He was short and stern. "We will close. No arguments. Close."

The little boy stood in the tiny store, surrounded by the customers who had come and bought the food Momma had made the last five years. He was barely able to see in the jam-packed space. His father, in his blood-stained apron holding a bottle of wine, his mother in her blue flowered apron, her eye still bruised and swollen.

His father's voice boomed, as if yelling at his friends would help keep him from crying. "Thank you for making this store a good store." His father wiped his eyes. "Thank you so very much. And to my wife, she made this happen. I was afraid." Now his voice cracked. "She made this happen. She is a good woman. A great woman. And I am a lucky man." He shook his head slowly, prompting the little boy to remember standing on the porch way up high watching Momma and Daddy and the little bird in the gutter working so hard on its nest. His father's voice trailed off. "So much work," he said, "she did everything."

The customers cheered. "Bravo! Bravo!"

A man with a red beard raised the little boy up so he could see. The little boy's father turned to his mother. He took her in his arms. He smiled and kissed her as gently as the little boy had ever seen.

His father raised a glass. "People gotta eat." He boomed in the tiny store. "They gotta eat."

A joyful but somber mood filled the air. The store began to empty.

"Wait!" He heard his mother say. "Wait."

She rushed to the front of the store, "Now you can leave."

And as the crowd began to disperse, they passed his mother standing in the doorway of Enzio's and Wife Italian Foods, in her blue flowered apron, handing everyone, as they filed out, a holy card, a statue, and a rosary.

Sketches of Northwest Side of Chicago Parish Carnivals

David Mathews

Our Lady of Victory, 1985. Eleven. We pulled up in a seventies avocado station wagon with a bad muffler. My family and I walked around to the music of Cyndi Lauper. We mostly went to see the carnival the way people look at the Christmas windows downtown—there was not enough money to go on more than one ride each. The kiddie ones where the cheapest—like the one that is little boats going in circles. As Lauper sang "Time After Time," I looked over my shoulder, while I prayed no one I knew would see me.

St. Bart's, 1990. Sixteen. The Tilt-A-Whirl spun as AC/DC sang of American thighs and my friends and I ran into Tina—the girl in my biology class that used to throw herself at me. After she walked away, my boys busted my balls for not wanting to fuck her—tall blonde headbanger rocking a tank top, stretchy jeans, and pirate boots. She scared me—she seemed to drink as much as my stepfather.

St. Pascal's, 1999. Twenty-five. My sisters wanted me to get out of the house. I ate elephant ears with extra sugar while Everlast played, and the Ferris Wheel lights blinked to the beat. I tried my hand at some game that involved throwing tennis balls into buckets—I knew I wasn't going to win anything. I just needed to throw something and forget about my being stuck in neutral life. "What It's Like" died down and I could hear cheesy carnival music faintly far off—like what I imagine mocking would sound like.

St. Ferdinand's, 2013. Thirty-nine. I needed a break from my own thoughts— we lived a block away from the parish. Pitbull was rapping about feeling the moment as a giant octopus spun people in the air. Jill and I walked, and I looked around at the kids with their parents, the teenager cliques, and the twenty-somethings on dates. They all looked like they were having fun. We were not moved to go on any of the rides.

The next morning, as I walked my dog Seamus, I took pictures of the ghost town of empty rides with my phone. They seem to be the same metal mechanical rides as when I was a kid—like no one makes them anymore or they make them the way people want to remember them looking. There is no music. Belmont has few cars on it—they sound more like a breeze than traffic. Around here, carnivals come every summer. Carnivals always remind me of things I cannot have.

The Parabola of a Single Bullet Shot into the Night Sky *Gint Aras*

I don't generally find beauty terrifying. In fact, my major issue with life is that so much is ugly while so little is gorgeous, that the vile outweighs the pleasant by billions of tons. So, I should have thought the sight of the most beautiful scene I had ever witnessed would leave me flooded with hope or grace. But that wasn't what happened.

This was in the mid-90's, back when my grandmother still lived in Marquette Park. I would go down there every month or so, visit her and wander through old neighborhood memories. This time I was tripping on three tabs of LSD, ingested in the park before I had decided to go for a long evening stroll. Sidewalks and lawns had already started going when I turned up the south end of an alley to face an Elysian scene.

Orange twilight was falling over broken glass, steel screws and shards of aluminum scattered about broken cement. Each shard of glass, the brown and green of beer bottles, clean silver of shattered car mirrors, pulsed and billowed. A trail of steel screws must have trickled from some unlucky bastard's shopping bag: they formed a lustrous narrow creek. Aluminum shards—some kid must have put a half-stick in a trash drum packed with cans—scattered the late evening light into a blazing dance: butterflies of flashing reflections synchronized to the chatter of lunatic sparrows in old man Garcia's plum tree.

I froze, desperate to hold on to the moment, knowing damn well I was experiencing the apex of my life. I'd never get back here—no beauty beyond this was possible, not for a mortal on planet earth. Ossified in an alley between Kedzie and Troy, south of 73rd, north of 74th, tears large as marbles fell from my face.

Alley scavengers in a pickup leaned on their horn to startle me out of their way. They must have been waiting some time for me to notice their truck. I moved to the side, and when the Mexicans flipped me the bird, I sensed they'd been sent by the universe to communicate: *Fuck you, Jake. This little scene is all you'll be getting tonight.*

Just like that, the zenith of my human experience had passed. I wandered the streets longing for it to return, even tried other alleys that might offer a second glimpse of heaven. But dusk had now given in to night. I was still tripping hard: the space around me seemed molten, streets reaching out as infinite pathways to everywhere but here. The scent of somebody's barbecue—sweet sauce and charring pork—wafted down Troy, mixing with the familiar scents of sugar and chocolate from the Nabisco factory. I wandered north to Marquette Park lagoon, where frogs hammered out their bass lines while locusts tore electric razors through the air. The surface of the water reflected Chicago's pink light pollution, wisps of clouds and low blinking planes gliding to land in Midway. I crossed a bridge to find my grandmother sitting in her lawn chair where I had left her near a softball diamond.

She was still listening to her Donavan tapes. But when I stood on the bottom step of noisy bleachers, she pushed her headphones off her meaty lobes. "I already peaked, Jakie," she said.

"Yeah, I peaked back in the alley over by Garcia's plum tree."

"Saw so many people walk by. That jagoff Frazier Thomas. Olivia Newton-John, lord, she's gained weight. I saw Jane Byrne, chain smoking crow." She guffawed. "Mayor, my ass. More like the honorable fucking exhaust manifold."

My grandmother kind of looked like W.C. Fields, down to speaking out the side of her mouth. Her gin blossom was dark as a rotten strawberry. She had drinking buddies all over the neighborhood, enjoyed a quart of Seagram's every Sunday after mass, and when all her church friends left, she'd invite neighbors to her backyard for a nightcap. Gram was presently showing me her empty pack of Pall Malls and her turquoise travel tumbler, once filled with Seagram's and Squirt, now collecting cigarette butts. "You see? Gram don't litter. Not like them fucking slobs over there." She pointed with her chin. "Dumped their baby's soiled diapers all over the park. Who raises these assholes?"

"You need more smokes and a refill?"

"Smokes, dammit, smokes, yeah. And not refill but re*fills*, re*fills*."

"You want me to go to a store?"

"Down 69th. That corner store gots Squirt for 99 cents. Then we head back to my place. You don't know it yet, but I got a surprise packed up for you."

"A surprise besides three tabs of acid?"

"Beside that, yeah. Beside it."

I didn't think much of any surprise. I figured it was a bag of bacon buns or coupons to Racine bakery she stole from church. I just went to the store, walking slow enough for her to waddle next to me as she pressed her cane into the soft grass.

She waited outside for me to get a fifth of Seagram's and a bottle of Squirt, a bag of ice and two packs of smokes. When Gram lit up, exhaling out her nose, she chewed the filter with her front dentures, something she only ever did while tripping. Then she leaned into her cane and walked with me to her bungalow on Talman, mumbling phrases the whole time, *All-star team of hugs, is what*, then, *Garage repairs, piece of shit,* and *A photo album with gray paper.* I had learned as a child never to ask for clarity. Her response was always the same: "If I tell you once but you can't figure it out, guess what? Tool shed."

We sat together on her porch. I poured drinks, keeping the supplies in a small cooler by our feet. Gram had all these Moroccan lanterns bought decades ago in a Beverly garage sale. I lit candles in each one to illuminate the porch, some of them hanging above us, others on the cement blocks of her bungalow's stairs. They cast speckles of red, blue and green light all over Gram's face and body, pencil-thin shards through the nebula of cigarette smoke that always lingered around her. "Now that's a nice night, no?" she exhaled, biting the filter. "Amazing, Jakie."

For a while we only sat taking it in. A delivery van lumbered by, then this biker ripped the stillness apart. Teenagers on their way to the park were smoking Swisher Sweets and playing *You down with O.P.P* on a boombox. They laughed and pushed each other into people's hedges. Gram yelled, "Should listen to Donavan, if you know what's good," but the kids ignored her.

The ashtray on a small table by her chair was heaping with butts. She tapped her cigarette over this heap and cleared her throat, indicating the mess needed cleaning. Gram kept a trash can just inside her front door—it was full of butts and empty bottles of Seagram's and Squirt. I dumped the tray and returned to my seat to notice the night now speckled with hundreds of fireflies.

The rhythm of the scene intensified, the fireflies multiplying, my interest and fascination heightened. Their tracers were synchronizing, falling diagonally—for a moment the night was raining yellow-green light. Then I noticed a boy on the other side of Talman, floating into my sight as darkness dissolved around him. He was catching the bugs, throwing them against the sidewalk and smearing them with his shoe to leave luminescent streaks.

"You never did that crap," Gram said. "You'd put 'em in jars, protected from punks like that over there. You'd set 'em free by the lagoon."

I was swishing gin and Squirt around my mouth. "Gram, something happened to me back there."

"Shit always happens back there."

"It was by Garcia's plum tree."

"That hairy goat should mow his lawn."

"I had this big vision. But now it's gone. I'm dying to bring it back."

"Yeah, Jakie." Gram sighed cigarette smoke all over herself. "Let me tell you about things we all want back. Live that way, you'll be somebody just wants all his shit back, never gets anything to keep. Know who that is? That's a write-off, all his shit in the pawn shop."

"I'm having a good trip. So I don't mean to bring us down. But the peak was so beautiful. I'll never have it back."

She crushed her cigarette in the tray, pulled out the handkerchief always stuffed in her sleeve, coughed and wiped her mouth. "Have what? What's *it?*"

"The gorgeous scene. All of it perfectly connected, the light and sparrows, and with such color and clarity... even garbage looked like heaven. I wanted to stay there. But the acid only gave me a glimpse."

She started laughing so hard it triggered a coughing fit. She had to wipe her mouth again, gulp her cocktail, light a cigarette to settle down. Then the laughter returned, the wrinkles around her eyes deepening, a tear caught in a fold between her nose and upper lip. "You poor dear..."

"But it was pretty intense, Gram."

142

Now she was squeezing the filter between two arthritic knuckles, her hand a tight fist. "Your grandfather got t-boned by a drunk when you were four. You ma's in the joint for life. Your dad's got kids in three states. You know his address?"

"What's he got to do with—"

"Listen, for Christ sakes. All them boys you knew in school. What are they on, and where? A bunch made their Reagan folks proud, KIA, home with flags on their caskets, heroes got a salute at their funeral, ma gets a picture for her wall. Others doin' time. There's some the same age as you, give you fries with a shake on Archer and Western. Those high school girlies? Child support this month—next month it's whoops, baby daddy got fired. I see that prom queen, you used to spooge in your dreams, now she weighs two-twenty, maybe two-thirty, plays scratch offs, and right by the register so I gotta wait for smokes when I'm on a nic-fit."

"Prom queen?"

"You know who I mean, Jakie. That girl peaked at eighteen. Her brothers peaked at eighteen, quarterback one, linebacker two. I weep for their ma. Carried mail all her life to get three burnouts? You wanna see downhill, Jakie? That's what downhill means."

"I was talking about the way—"

"Before they give out them degrees in Carbondale, don't they give no test to check if you got IQ?" Gram tried to fake a Benny Hill accent: *"The best hallucination of my life happened by a plum tree, doctor, and now I'm depressed.* Jakie, you were tripping brains in an alley. If that's the best your life's ever gonna give, then pucker up and kiss a holy angel. Thirty seconds of acid heaven beats anything your ma ever got."

"But I still—"

"Still still still…with you it's *still.* What you *still* need to do is quit shellin' out coin for that damn shrink. Fills your brain with Mrs. Butterworth's. Why not lift weights? Join boxing, get a punching bag, punch someone in the head, get punched in the face. On my mama's grave, I swear a shrink is horseshit. I see them talk their crap on TV. All them shows got one now. They let another suburban nag whine. Yeah, her life's bad here, her life's bad there, but she's got a hundred bucks of makeup on her face, five hundred bucks of thread on her well-fed ass. Then the shrink—can see plain in his face, he's a damn drunk—he looks in a camera with fancy talk, *it's your copilot bi polar bear.* The truth is way more simple: *you're forty years old, so grow the fuck up.* Act like an adult. Wanna count this bitch's blessings, better hire IBM. All them shows just constipate my runs. And this damn drink is empty, Jakie," she handed me her glass. "A little stronger this time. Two fingers, at least."

Gram's rants could hit below the belt—she knew I was ashamed to be in treatment for depression—but they could also calm me, because deep down I mostly agreed with the essence of what she said. Still, I didn't want to hear it while tripping on her porch during a firefly storm. Pouring Squirt onto the ice and gin, I thought she was preparing more of her refrains—*you work in a firm, Jakie,* and *you got a house in Old Town.* But when I handed her the drink, she toasted one of the lanterns. "Here's to your glow," Gram said, and she smiled into its red shine. Then she slurped the drink to ask me, "When you wanna see your surprise?"

"Is it a bag of hunter's sausage or something?"

"You nuts? This surprise is serious. Just in the garage. You come with me, you'll see it yourself."

I followed her down the gangway to the back of the property, holding her by the shoulders in the dark. She almost tripped over a snoozing cat that shrieked and scampered off. I picked her cane off the ground and guided her further. Then she fumbled with her keys so that I'd take them from her to let us inside.

The garage was empty as always, the same musty boxes, the same old jugs, mouse shit along the walls. Pa's tools were hanging right where he'd left them forty-two years ago. Save for grime and rust, they hung exactly as they had the night he took his green 1950 Olds to go for smelt but ended up in a casket. Except for clothing donated to thrifts, following his funeral, Gram had never touched any of Pa's things. For over four decades, she kept Pa's attic darkroom locked from everyone, though primarily from herself. My silent curiosity over the attic had become as normal as my understanding that it would never be satisfied. Out of respect for Gram, and maybe out of pity, I never asked questions or begged to go up there.

The wooden box and leather briefcase caught my eye. They were on a narrow worktable near the garage window, right where the tools had been hung. "It's that," said Gram. "It's them things for you right there."

The box contained a thick photo album. In the pale light of the garage, I could not make them out too well, but some were self-portraits of Pa by wooden walls, others of him and Gram: here they were in a row boat,

144

and another showed them in the back of a hay wagon. Some were of frost patterns in windows, or crisp leaves fallen to puddles. But the most fascinating were of people I did not know, had never seen. I flipped though gray pages of over one hundred photographs hung with corner mounts, and beside each photo was a description written in Pa's tight, clean handwriting. *Father and mother by the sunflowers, Stephenson, Michigan, Summer, 1941.* There were pictures of funerals, of my great grandparents, ghosts visiting me in a South Side garage.

"Open Pa's briefcase."

Inside, the case was split in half with a narrow strip of balsa wood. On one side lay a tobacco pipe, two ornate, pearl-colored fountain pens, three thin gold bracelets, a folded bellows camera and a copper letter opener. On the other side was money: eight straps of 100-dollar bills, then twenties and tens held by bronze money clips. A cloth pouch was full of rare coins.

I reached for the letter opener first, oddly violent and sharp, oddly peaceful and elegant, obviously old, yet nothing so new had ever been introduced to me. Gram said, "I gone through his stuff."

"It has his initials on it…"

"Finally gone through it. Was scared, find photos of his women, pictures of boobs. Yeah, I thought he had women. What the hell, was always out somewhere, said he had pictures to take. Never showed me none of 'em. Instead, I look in here, find out he was savin' up somehow, illegal or legal, I dunno. And he was keepin' the story of his family, the story of me and him, collected photos from his folks, times we went up in Wisconsin, the U.P. You flip through there, find pictures of your ma when she's a kid, photos of them together with your dad.

"All them's for you, Jakie. Use the money smart, please, not on no shrinks or no gold diggers. You're educated, so do right with it. Them photos—it's more than I can see without a crushed heart—they go way back. Maybe you can figure out how far back, who them people are from your Pa's life, since I don't know. He worked private. Upstairs, the whole place is unlocked now, you'll find lots more. Lots and lots more… albums and envelopes. Diaries." She was twisting her cane into the ground. "Now come outside 'cause I don't wanna be in this garage no more."

We went to stand in the middle of her yard, in the patch of grass where I used to play with Tonka trucks, where I had splashed around in a kiddie pool almost every weekend of my summers. The nebula of smoke formed around her again, pink from Chicago's light pollution. "I finally gone through it," she said. "Nobody know it yet, only you."

Just a moment before she had said those words, someone somewhere east of us, perhaps by the train yard, perhaps they were much closer, pointed a .300 magnum rifle into the sky and fired a shot. The bullet rose above Chicago, high enough to vantage the criss-crossed lines of streets lit up by amber lamps, the pools of cool light falling onto parking lots, and the red streaks of brake lights, the white streams of headlights, the dark patches of parks, forest preserves, hospital gardens, the yard behind St. Casimir's nunnery and next to Maria High School. As the bullet peaked and crested, it fell back to the city along the elegant curve of a parabola, whose end found itself directly in the center of the backyard on Talman, where it entered Gram's nebula of smoke to pierce her directly through the top of the forehead and lodge itself in her throat.

She fell before me like a tree. I knelt there in the grass, slapping her cheeks, pressing her wrists, the wind knocked out of me, my hands buzzing as though I had been handling a jack hammer.

The autopsy found the bullet, but it was never connected to any rifle, never to any report of a shot fired into the night. I had not heard any pop, and neither had any neighbor. Gram was, it turned out, in relatively good health, advancing osteoporosis, some clogging in her arteries, a strained liver, filthy lungs, but they told me she might have lived another decade, maybe more. They also told me, shrugging their shoulders, rubbing their chins, that all bullets fired into Chicago nights end up coming back down—that's just a basic law of physics—but almost all of them fall harmlessly, and they land in places where no one ever finds them.

Bunny and Other Matters
Keith Peterson

The old lady was very hard of hearing, very firm in her manner, and had said her name was Bunny. The proof, if one wanted proof, was in each of the rather heavy coffee table books she had trundled over in a vinyl shopping bag—each had a bookplate that said Bunny. A cartoon picture of a rabbit drove home the point. Seth was trying to explain that the big Leonardo Da Vinci volume, even though it was very big, was a fairly common and difficult to sell book. Something similar, if not worse, could be said for the boxed set of *The Writer's America/The Artist's America* published by *American Heritage* magazine. She had explained that her daughter had been taking boxes of her books to Half Price but that they didn't give much for them. She thought these two books were better and hoped to get more than Half Price would pay. She was going to have to move into a smaller place now, she had explained, and she had all these books. Bunny was eighty. She mentioned that more than once.

Seth let her talk, as he didn't like shouting and that was the only way she could hear him. It seemed like she was used to being the one who talked. But, in the end, he had to disappoint her expectations.

"I'm sorry, but I can only give five dollars for this Leonardo book, and," Seth lifted up the practically unsellable boxed set, hating to make her carry it back, not wanting to buy it, not wanting to argue about the price of it, especially in the loud voice which would be required, "for this, I'm afraid, I could only pay two dollars. Like I said— even though they are large books, they're not much in demand."

"Not much in demand? Leonardo?" Bunny seemed genuinely taken aback.

"This particular book, I mean," Seth almost shouted. "For some

147

reason, people don't seem to want it. Maybe it's too big. It doesn't fit on a bookshelf unless you lay it flat, and then it takes up all this room. And the illustrations are, I don't know, kind of dull. Kind of muddy. Not crisp. It's not Leonardo's fault."

"I was sure a book like that would be worth more than five dollars. It cost twenty-five when I bought it. I suppose you know what you're doing, but it doesn't seem like much." She paused, frowning. "I have to decide whether it's worth taking them back and trying somewhere else." She picked the Leonardo book up and opened it, leaning it on the desk. "I don't see that well anymore either," Bunny said, peering at the open pages.

"Well," she said with finality, "you're not giving me as much as I expected, but I don't want to carry them back. I'll sell them to you."

Seth paid her, and she took about five minutes to fold the vinyl bag just right and put it in her purse. While that was going on, Seth caught sight of the girl with the Hello Kitty backpack browsing in the fiction section, doing a good job of pretending not to have overheard the transaction and suppressing her amusement.

When Bunny was ready to go, Seth helped her up the stairs— mostly by going up behind her step by step, ready to catch her if she fell backwards. It was a case where courtesy was deeply entangled with fear of lawsuits.

The girl with the Hello Kitty backpack came up to the desk a few minutes later with an Iris Murdoch paperback and one by Julian Barnes— *Flaubert's Parrot.*

"Thanks again for calling in about my door this morning," Seth said as he used the calculator to add up the total. "It's turning into a crazy day. I thought having the party tonight would be stressful enough."

"Oh, I didn't mind doing it," she said. "It seemed a shame, you know, all that broken glass and mess. Did they steal much from you?"

Seth laughed. "They stole my cash register. My new cash register that I didn't like anyway. Or, I should say, he did. It was empty, so all that's missing is the stupid cash register. Good riddance."

The girl started to speak, stopped, and smiled. "Two strange things— correct me if I'm wrong. Somebody stole your empty cash register but you don't mind because you didn't like it?" She sounded genuinely amused and puzzled.

"Well— I did mind the damage to the door and the feeling of being invaded. You know that helpless feeling of rage you get after a break-in? So,

I did mind, in that way. But, the register— oh, it's a long story and not that interesting."

"You said not they but he took it. He took it. So— you know who broke in?"

"I'm pretty sure I do. I could explain that too, and make myself look pretty stupid while I do, if you'd like."

"Sure." She smiled again. Seth wondered if this was flirtation. Life had taught him that he never really knew.

"OK— well, you see, ever since I started out some twenty years ago, I've always used this desk drawer here," he pulled it out of the massive desk so she could see, "as a cash drawer. This great aircraft carrier of a desk was a lucky find I made just weeks before I opened my first store, and I've always been quite fond of it. And for all these years, until a few months ago, I never had a problem with anyone stealing from it."

"But now you do."

"Oh yeah. A vindictive little creep. And now, it seems, he's mad because he couldn't steal anymore when I got the register."

"And now the register is gone," she said, nodding.

"Right. And now all the money is in my pockets and I'm back to using this old calculator. It's not very convenient, especially with the coins. I can't even use the desk for coins because he'll find a way to steal them. It's happened more than once."

"Quite the master criminal," she said. "What about the police?"

"Yeah, them. I've called them each time, though I wonder what the point is. They take a report. They look at me like I'm a total idiot. When it happened again, they acted like it was my fault and just told me to get a register. They weren't very sympathetic. Rolled their eyes and all that. And today— they barely kept from laughing today taking the report on the stolen register."

"Well— that's not nice," she said. And after a pause, "Still, it does have its humorous aspects."

"I know. Thanks. I told you it wasn't a story that would redound to my credit."

"Redound," she said, savoring the word, "That's a word we don't use often enough."

She looked off into the distance. "I'm going to see if I can use it in a sentence sometime soon."

"It can also mean something with the action of waves— you know, like to swell or surge and like that. You *never* hear it used that way nowadays."

"Give me an example," she said, smiling impishly.

"Oh great— a pop quiz." Seth thought for a minute. "I don't know. OK— here's a line from Pope, I don't remember from what— wait a second, it's coming: *Round the descending nymph the waves redounding roar.* How about that? Nice use of an alliterative R by our man Alexander to give us the sound of the water."

"How did you do that?" She sounded impressed.

"I don't know. There are things in my head. Sometimes they can even prove of use, if I can retrieve them. OK— that's one. What was the other strange thing? I think we only covered one so far."

"Oh, right. You said you were having a party and that— something like you found the idea stressful."

"Well, sure. Don't you find throwing a party a bit of a trial?"

"Isn't the idea of having a party to have fun?"

"That's one theory, I guess."

Suddenly Seth realized that there was an awkward pause happening. "By the way— would you like to come to said party? Perhaps there would be a redounding of fun if you could be there."

"OK— that was twice. I don't think you want to do that. And, was that really proper usage?"

"In the obsolete meaning? I think so, really. But, it does sound a bit forced for anyone who's not William F. Buckley Jr."

The door opened and Toy came down the stairs holding a couple of book club edition romance novels, the dust jackets featuring ladies in diaphanous nightwear in front of castles. He had found them in a box in an alley a few blocks away, along with some battered VCR tapes.

"It says you buy books," Toy said.

"It does say that."

Seth eyed the books without even handling them.

"I'm not buying those. If you want to sell books to bookstores, you have to make the effort to be able to tell one from another. To know what a bookstore like this might be looking to pay money for. See what I mean?"

Toy placed one on the desk next to the display of plastic laminated bookmarks.

"What's wrong with this one?"

"Everything. Sorry, but I'm not giving lessons here on how to scout books. You want to do that, you figure it out on your own."

"All right. I was just askin'." He bumped the display taking back the book, knocked it over, put the books down again as he gathered up the spilled bookmarks, palmed one while setting the rest in a neat pile, took his books and went up the stairs and out the door.

"My life and welcome to it," said Seth.

"Did you notice he stole one of your bookmarks?"

"He did? Just now?"

"Yeah just now. I wonder what that was all about. I don't think he's worried about losing his place in *Love's Lonely Palace*."

"You saw him take a bookmark?"

The girl looked at him and arched an eyebrow. "Maybe we're working together."

"Then I'm doomed. Doomed..." Seth shook his head, smiling with unexpected pleasure. The bookmarks were practically giveaways. He didn't care.

"Oh, cheer up, Hamlet. What about this party you were talking about?"

"Right — that's tonight. Should be quite the social stunner. An old friend of mine is debuting her book of oddly endearing poems and songs about cats and other subjects. I think she's going to do a reading, there will be refreshments and noise and colorful characters. I bet you'd have a good time— I'll introduce you to all the celebrities."

"There'll be celebrities, will there?"

"Actually, you never know. Our friend Peter, who drives the mini-cam van for one of the television stations is coming, and who knows who he might talk into checking out the scene. He seems to know everybody. So does Shoshonna, for that matter."

"Shoshonna?"

"It's her book party."

"What time does all this get going?"

"The invitations say 8 PM, so that must be the time."

There was another little awkward pause.

"You know," Seth said, "I don't know your name."

"I know you don't," the girl said, smiling. "I was wondering how you were going to introduce me."

"Er— I would say 'Shoshonna, this is my new friend...' and then pause expectantly."

"Ah. My new friend," said the girl.

"I would supply a name if I had one."

"Allison."

"Allison..." Seth hinted, with a slight nod, an eyebrow, and assorted other subtle body language, that he wished to know her last name.

"Martin. Allison Martin."

"I'm very pleased to make your acquaintance, Allison Martin."

"And you must be," she picked up one of his business cards and squinted at it, "Seth Pearson? Is that right?"

"At your service."

"And since we're gathering up names and filing them in the proper place, the name of the book is...?"

"The book is called *That's Why I Bite*."

She smiled with her eyes. "I like that. Can you quote me any?"

"Well— as to that. Shoshonna reads her stuff very well and I can't match her style. Especially with the ones having to do with cats and other creatures."

"Other creatures?"

"There's one about large rodents."

"Oh dear. Do any involve people?"

"Some do. Not that many, actually. Let me think."

Seth looked slightly sad. "Here's one. Or some lines from one:

He knew that birds on a wire
could be musical notation,
knew the Muse
might be dancing backwards,
riding on big sister's shoes,
red gold hair flung back,
laughing."

"Who's the 'he' in that," she asked, noting the melancholy now in Seth's eyes.

"That was our friend, our late friend, Zeno. He was an artist, a poet, a glorious eccentric."

"I like it," she said simply. And then "You miss him?"

"You would too."

"Well. It sounds like we have much to catch up on."

"So, you'll come?"

"Wouldn't miss it, Seth Pearson."

"That's great news, Allison. My day is made."

"Good. Well, I better get back to my job, or there might be trouble. I'll see you tonight."

She gathered up her two books and went up the stairs. Seth felt himself not minding at all, for some reason, the fact that his door had been smashed that morning.

You Shall See the Face of God and Live   *Caitlin Garvey*

In 1998, when I was in fourth grade, Momma wrote a journal entry that discusses her impending chemotherapy treatment for her leukemia:

> *Surprise. There is to be no treatment, at least not until after the holidays. I'm relieved, but a large part of me is angry. Last week was pure hell. I met with friends to "organize" in the event things went badly. I felt stripped bare. I felt as if my life and lifestyle were under critical scrutiny. It also made me fear for the girls. In the days that followed up to the doctor's appointment, I couldn't sleep much, and when I could, I had horrible nightmares about the children. I lost five pounds. I was terrified.*
> *And now it's over. Momentarily. I feel myself being sucked into depression. I'm annoyed by everyday events. I'm tired. I'm having difficulty adjusting to dealing with these days that I hadn't planned on dealing with. I'm confused. I feel fat and sluggish. I don't know what to do. I fear going forward and having to face the treatment option again...*
> *I can't hide from this disease or the feelings I have about it. I*

can't try to be what others, or more aptly, what I think others
want from me. I just have to be myself and accept it, with all
its inadequacies and strengths. I need to repair. I can't repair
the disease or my body, but I can repair my relationships, which
are worn thin by the stress of this ordeal.
I've worked so many years on improving my mind. Now I need
to work on the emotions that I have so skillfully hidden.

That year, my class was preparing to receive the Sacrament of Reconciliation, and we learned that there were different kinds of sins: big and small ones, mortal and venial. "Mortal sin is like a malignant tumor that critically hurts our spiritual life and our relationship with God," our religion teacher repeated each week. Small sins included gossip and accidental swearing, and big sins included things like murder, sacrilege, divorce, and suicide. I was particularly scared of the "sin of omission"— a small sin with the potential to become a big one— so I made sure to tell Momma everything, even things that I'd promised my classmates I'd keep secret, like that John's older brother had shown him the sex scene in *Friday the 13th*, or that Kelly had stolen $5 from her mother's purse to buy candy bars, or that Matt had forged his dad's signature on his behavioral report card. I wanted to have to confess as few things as possible to the priest, with the goal that he would consider me a "good" person and would relay that message to God. Although I hadn't seen Momma's journals, I could still sense that she was worried about something— she was more irritable than usual, she seemed to have less energy and expressed less excitement when I told her about my school day, and her hugs were longer and more frequent. I believed that if God thought I was "good," then he'd be able to make Momma healthy and keep my family safe.

On the day we were going to receive the Sacrament, my fourth-grade class lined up to confess our sins to a priest who was sitting in the corner of the church behind a portable screen. When it was my turn, I anxiously told the priest that I was jealous of how much attention my parents were giving my older sister, and I waited for him to say a prayer. Instead, he said, loudly, "I'm sorry, dear. I didn't hear you. Could you speak up?" I tried repeating my sin, but he interrupted my plea for forgiveness with a sneeze, and then he delivered a rushed prayer. "God forgives you," he said, and then added, "You can signal for the next person in line." When I walked back to my pew, I thought of *The Wizard of Oz* and how I shouldn't trust people who hid behind screens, and I wondered what was so special about this priest that gave him the power to talk to God directly.

A barrier grew between God and me, a barrier that grew even bigger when I was a sophomore in high school and Momma was diagnosed with breast cancer. The sicker she got, the less I cared about appealing to a God who was allowing it to happen — Momma's kind of malignancy didn't stem from any kind of sin. I cared about her approval, not God's.

Eventually, though, a barrier between Momma and me grew, too. The summer following my freshman year of college, I sat beside Momma's hospice bed, and as I gave her ice chips and applied more gauze to her wound, I felt an urgent need to have her "see" me. Even though I'd kept things from her so that she could focus on getting better instead of on the family's well-being, I still wanted her to know everything about me before it was too late. I wanted to confess that I'd lied to her about having a boyfriend, and that I'd made him up because I didn't want anyone to think that I was gay. I wanted her to be the first person to know that I really was gay. I wanted to tell her that I had a crush on my best female friend, and I wanted to know what she thought I should do about it. I wanted to tell her that I'd been feeling lost and lonely, and that I'd skipped several days of school for the first time in my life. I wanted to ask her what it felt like to really love someone. I wanted to confess that I'd lied to her when I said I was having a great time at college and was making a lot of new friends, and I wanted to confess that when I told her I was going to dorm parties, I was really in my own dorm room watching *Titanic* on loop, pausing it right before the ship hits the iceberg and then rewinding to the beginning. I wanted to tell her that because I was questioning both my sexuality and my belief in God, I felt out of place as a student at a large Catholic university. I wanted to admit that when I texted her from my campus that I was going for a swim, I was really going to the dining hall and binge eating until I felt better; that my dorm's resident assistant had written me a "warning letter" because I was crying too loudly in the common room one night after I'd gotten drunk by myself; that I was having trouble picking a major because I couldn't picture myself existing in the future; that I was having night terrors about her death. But as I watched Momma struggle to move, and I heard her whine from pain, my confessions seemed small, insignificant, and selfish, so instead I said nothing.

During my time at college and my summer at home, Momma failed to confess certain things to me, too: the frequency of her emergency room trips and the duration of her hospital stays; the reason my dad was sleeping in the basement; the reasons she cried every night. We both avoided telling each other about wounds that weren't visible, our confessions remaining behind our screens.

When you walk into the rectory of Saint Pascal's Parish in Chicago, you'll see a small drawn rendering of Jesus. It's on top of parish brochures on a side table. It's a classic image of him— his skin is white, and he has long brown hair and a beard. The drawing cuts off at his neckline. He has brown eyes that are looking down— he looks sad, even a little lonely. It almost looks like a high school senior portrait, but one of the outtakes, the headshots parents don't bother to put in a nice frame or order in a larger size.

I'm sitting in a chair across from Jesus's picture as I wait for Father Thomas Dore to talk with me. After staring at his portrait for a few minutes, I start to feel sad for him. Maybe he got rejected from his top choice college. Or no one took him to prom. The atmosphere of the rectory makes me a little sad, too. It's monochromatic, each piece of furniture a light beige to match the walls, and I sit directly outside an office room. The office door is closed, but I can still overhear a priest complain to his rectory assistant that she shouldn't have scheduled him to preside over tomorrow's early morning baptism. I hear him sigh right before his assistant opens the door and walks past me. I look at the analog clock that hangs above Jesus. Father Dore is five minutes late.

I can't remember the first time I met Father Dore, but I must have been four or five years old. Father Dore was the pastor at St. Giles Catholic Parish for most of my grade school years, and he made a point of getting to know the families. He frequently came over to our house for dinner on Sunday nights, and after dinner he usually stayed for the new episode of *Malcolm in the Middle*— my whole family watched it together on the couch downstairs. Often, he fell asleep during the 30-minute episode, and Sarah (because the rest of us called "seniority" to get out of doing anything unpleasant) was charged with the task of waking him up. She tapped him gently on his shoulder, and if he didn't respond to that, she shook his shoulder with her hand.

Dore is now eighty-one years old and retired, and he walks toward me with a limp. Though the last time I saw him was nine years ago when he presided over Momma's funeral, he looks the same as I remember him— tall and confident, with a full head of white hair, a short, white beard, and glasses with small, squared frames. There are only a few differences in his appearance: he has a hearing aid in his left ear, and he isn't wearing a collar. He's wearing a navy-blue button-down shirt with black dress pants, but even without the collar, his presence still intimidates me, and I'm worried about how he'll perceive me. I never spoke much to him when he visited our house, so even when he was at our dinner table, I still felt as distant from him as I did when he was at the altar, and I was in the pew. I wonder if he expects that I still frequently attend church— he knows, from my dad, that I attended Notre Dame, so maybe he expects that the two of us will bond over our knowledge of Scripture. I pull down the right sleeve of my sweater to hide my forearm tattoo from him— a religion teacher at St. Giles condemned tattoos as "impure and immoral"— and I smile widely at him as he apologizes for his lateness. He says it's his "off-day," so he was at the dentist— even though he's retired, he still frequently has tasks to perform, his "on-days." As he leads me into the room that the first priest and his assistant had exited, he apologizes for walking slowly. "Back problems," he says, and then laughs, "Comes with old age."

He didn't seem this physically weak on the day of Momma's funeral. He didn't have a limp; he walked steady, with purpose, and above her coffin, he held up the heavy Gospel without wavering.

Before we sit down in the meeting room, Dore hugs me, and his arms— as thin as a teenage girl's but without any muscle mass— shake a little as he wraps them around me. I wonder if the Gospel is too heavy for him to carry now. I don't want to put my arms all the way around him, fearing I will hurt him. It's an uncomfortable hug, like hugging the grandma on your dad's side, the one who always notices the stain on your shirt even when it's covered by a cardigan— the hug seems mandatory although it comforts neither person, and even after it's over and you release, you still live in that hug for minutes afterward, her strong floral perfume sticking to your sweater.

Father Dore was a witness to Momma's suffering. He was at our house in her final days, praying beside her hospice bed and administering the Eucharist. It's typical for laypeople, or un-ordained clergy, to do this work, but Father Dore did it because he was so close to our family. The church refers to the administration of the Holy Eucharist to the sick as *Viaticum*, meaning "food for the journey," with the idea that death is a journey into the afterlife. Anointing of the Sick is one of the two Sacraments of Healing— Reconciliation is the other— and it's performed to remind parishioners that when one person is sick, the entire community is wounded. I remember Father Dore's face as he laid the Eucharist on Momma's tongue— he didn't seem surprised by how sick Momma looked, or by the hospice attachments, and he didn't have pity in his eyes— he looked serious, certain and powerful, like he had a job to do, and he was going to finish it. I remember doubting, but still hoping, that his hands could heal her.

Even when I was younger, I don't think I ever felt absolutely sure that God existed. I couldn't picture him, so he seemed distant and unfamiliar. I never knew what to say to him, and when I did pray, it seemed like a chore, as did going to church every Sunday. The constant repetition of church didn't allow for much creativity— the service dictated our responses. "The Lord be with you," Father Dore would say, and everyone in the congregation would robotically respond, "And also with you." Although St. Giles cycled through a few cantors per year, they all sang the same songs each Sunday, and they all had raspy, untrained voices. One cantor was completely tone-deaf, and my sisters and I would groan when we saw her walk up to the microphone for the responsorial psalm on her assigned Sundays. I prayed before I went to bed each night when I was in grade school, but instead of saying the "Our Father," I usually just asked for things and waited to see if I got them the next day. I asked for extra candy in my lunch, an "I love you" note from a grade-school crush, and an A on a math test, and I saw God as just one big disappointment when I didn't get anything I asked for.

I craved the certainty that Father Dore seemed to have. Whenever he gave a homily, his voice boomed throughout the church. The boom was like an imperative— I always interpreted it as, "Follow my message... or else"— and I remember being scared by it. I wanted to hide under the pew to escape it. Instead, many Sundays, the children of the congregation were called up to the altar to sit around Father Dore as he delivered his homily, and he directed it specifically at us. He would look at each kid and say, "You are God's chosen one." Other times he'd wag his finger at one of us and warn, "Listen to your parents." Because I was a quiet, nervous, and insecure kid, a loud voice, to me, indicated a level of "truth"— the louder the voice, the truer the words.

In the same 1998 journal, Momma wrote:

My white blood cell count is higher, but not frighteningly so. My thyroid is probably the cause of my recent exhaustion; I'll pick up the prescription tomorrow.

For a religion assignment, Meaghan and I talked about what God means to me. She really seemed to understand my explanation, and as part of the assignment, put it into words and an abstract collage about water. It was great art and a real pleasure that she understood what I said.

Was Momma's God like water, something tangible but not a "person"? Did her idea of God change as she got sick or closer to death? I wonder if Father Dore, as he put the Eucharist to her lips, could gauge her degree of certainty about God, or if he could sense what she thought about life after death.

"Many things are blurry about when my mom was in hospice," I say to him, my voice a bit shaky, as we sit across from each other. "But I remember your face. I remember you being there."

He nods and then says, "You know, dealing with the issues of health and death is the hardest part of being a priest." He runs his fingers through his beard, like he's thinking carefully about what to say next. His homilies always lasted longer than the other priests', but he rarely repeated things, judicious in his word choice and precise about the message. He says, "Your mother's funeral is on the list of top three most difficult ones over which I've presided." It's second, he says, after the Barnett baby, Paige, who died at 18 months from a "lightning quick invasion" of Streptococcus pneumoniae. Keith Barnett, Paige's dad, had gone to wake Paige up from her nap and found her lying in her crib, blue. Ranking third is the funeral of Father Dore's close friend, whose name he doesn't say, who died abruptly in a car accident.

I'm a little taken aback that he's ranked Momma's funeral second. I remember him saying, quietly, "I'll help if I can," when I called to ask about meeting for our interview. Maybe he feels that he won't be helpful to me if he doesn't express how much Momma's death affected him. But I wonder about his relationship to her. I don't remember it being particularly special. She sometimes laughed at him for falling asleep during *Malcolm in the Middle*, and she frequently commented on his bad table manners— he used to clink his silverware together a few times before cutting up the food on his plate. Dore was always much closer to my dad. The two of them still go out to dinner, movies, or basketball games. Why would Momma's funeral rank above Father Dore's close friend's? But as I stare at him from across the room, I think about the peace that certainty must bring, and I stop myself from asking him why he feels this way. I choose, instead, for the first time since grade school, to take his word for it.

Father Dore shifts from the topic of health and death to his role as a retired pastor. He talks about the different religious retreats he's gone to in his retirement and about his daily activities within the church. He says he periodically helps out at both St. Pascal and St. Giles, delivering the occasional homily, listening to confessions, and talking one-on-one with parishioners who have specific concerns or who are having crises of faith. But his knees are weak, so he can't kneel during the Communion rite, and even standing for prolonged periods is painful for him, so recently he's been getting fewer calls to help out.

He grew up down the street from St. Pascal, and he says that it "feels funny" to be back in this neighborhood after so many years. He talks about his childhood— his parents' involvement in the church and their role in his "faith journey." Both of his parents were very active in the church, and at a young age, Dore became an altar server. He tells me that ever since he was a kid, he felt that one day he would have a big role in the church. He talks about his seminary training at Quigley Preparatory in downtown Chicago, and how at home he felt there. "I knew that the Lord wanted me," he says, "and he was calling me home. I felt his presence, and I thought, *I'm not going to argue with him.*"

As Father Dore talks about his relationship to God, I realize that part of me feels desperate to relate to him, like I'm a child who wants her parents' approval and consolation. I can't explain exactly why, but I want Father Dore to like me. Maybe there's a part of me that still believes he can relay my "goodness" to God, and that God could grant me happiness as a result. There's still a part of me that hopes I'm wrong to be skeptical of God's existence.

After a brief silence, Father Dore decides it's his turn to ask me questions. When he asks about the Chicago neighborhood, Edgewater, where I live, and how often I go to church, I'm afraid to tell him that I stopped going a long time ago. I stutter and then mumble something about not knowing if there was even a church by me. He raises an eyebrow and then asks about my cross street. When I answer, he says, "There's a church right by you, right on Broadway. The old gothic one. It's right there." When I respond with, "Oh, that's right," he gives me a strange look, then rests his chin between his thumb and index finger and says, "I think you're overdue for a homily."

The boom begins. It feels even more overwhelming in this small room, just the two of us. He has different concerns today than he had during the old homilies I remember: "We're getting and receiving, and we're not focused on giving," he says. "It's all, 'Buy this now at a cheaper price.' It's bigger this, bigger that— a bigger bed, a bigger car, a bigger phone— stuff to make you look better and nicer." He looks down for a minute at my iPhone, which is recording the interview from the table between us. "Do we really need the iPhone 7?" he asks. "What happens to it all when there's the next big thing? It winds up in your attic, or your basement, or your storage unit. Where does our faith come in?"

He continues, "People try to find meaning in things like sex, fame, and money, but what they really need is God." He talks about drug and alcohol addiction as a misplaced longing for God, and then he adds, "Suicide is a longing, too. People long to stop feeling empty, so they turn to sinful things."

As he says this, I picture Tammy, the nurse who'd been assigned to me after my overdose, handing me a Styrofoam cup filled with charcoal and saying, "Drink this. It will save your life." I was in my junior year at Notre Dame, not fully two years after Momma died, when I ended up in a South Bend hospital after my suicide attempt: I had ingested 30 Ambien pills, 10mg each. Tammy stared at me as I stared down at the charcoal: a black residue, ash-like and porous, the remains of the campfire I attended in the woods when I was sixteen and drunk for the first time the night after Momma had a double mastectomy; the blackness at the bottom of the bowl that I used to smoke weed before a school presentation because, as I told myself, it worked better than anti-anxiety medications; the thickness of the cement parking spot in the alley where my first girlfriend and I carved our names, not just as an act of rebellion but also a chance to declare ourselves as a gay couple, carving our identities to feel more at ease with them; the black ink that the tattoo artist wiped off my forearm as he finished Max's crown from Maurice Sendak's *Where the Wild Things Are*, a book Momma used to read to me when I was little. Hours later, long after I'd thrown out the empty cup, I rushed to the bathroom— a side-effect of charcoal consumption— and vomited up what took me so long to get down, a long and huge release, a vomit so uncontainable that it sprayed in a web-like pattern over the toilet bowl, black matter zigzagging and striping the white seat, expelling death and creating a mess of memory.

Dore pauses his homily, and we sit in silence for a moment as I study him. He looks lonely, and there's a kind of desperation about him. Maybe he's needed someone to talk to for a while. Maybe he's sad or even depressed, living in a small room in a rectory where, eventually, maybe even soon, he'll die. Most days he just sits with his thoughts. I get the sense from our interview that he communicates every once in a while with his sister, but he has no other living family and only a few friends. He doesn't have a personal phone, and he doesn't use the Internet. He considers my dad a close friend, and he says he's marked on his calendar when they're going out for dinner next— but that's eight weeks from now. He's missed having an audience, I think.

I wonder what he longs for. I wonder, too, what he isn't confessing to me, and I wonder if he avoids thinking about some aspects of health and death because they threaten his certainty. Does he get anxious, too? Does he stay up at night, unable to shut off his mind? Is he able to acknowledge some of the contradictions in the church's doctrine? I wonder if he's ever seen *The Wizard of Oz*, and I wonder if he felt sad, like I did, when Dorothy finds out that the Wizard is just an ordinary old man.

As Father Dore's voice fades to the background, the voices of my memories increase, and I think more about the things that Momma and I didn't say to each other and the moment her body was wheeled out of the bedroom. I prayed to God when she was in hospice. I apologized to him for neglecting prayer for years, but once again I was asking him for something— Momma's life. And again, he didn't deliver. But in the moments before Momma's death, even after my dad had administered the morphine and she was incoherent, I'd convinced myself that she'd get better. I told myself that she wouldn't die, over and over again, until it sounded true.

I feel my face growing hotter with the anger that I still harbor about her death, and my desire to impress Father Dore begins to fade. Where was his God when Momma, at age fifty-two, was lowered into the ground? Where was God when my fifteen-year-old sister watched as Momma was carried out of the house in a body bag? Many of the adults at Momma's wake told me that she would always be with me, but when I pray to her, she doesn't answer.

I scream at the silence.

Each June, on the anniversary of her death, my family returns to Queen of Heaven cemetery, and we sit on the grass beside her grave. We say, "Hi, we miss you." I don't believe anymore that the shining sun is her saying "hi" back, and I don't believe that, like Jesus, she'll rise from the dead. Father Dore's Eucharist didn't do anything to heal her.

I think of Jesus after he's condemned to death, his back covered with lashes, his head crowned with thorns, carrying a heavy cross on his bruised shoulders. I think of the huge nails hammered through his hands and feet. He bleeds heavily, his arms outstretched, his believers witnesses to the horror of it all. I prayed for a miracle, and instead there was just that cross, and all that blood.

I can feel sweat dripping down my face as my mind flashes the events of my freshman year in college— the frequency of gay bashings on campus, the sociology professor who was fired by the university president for coming out to a fellow professor as a gay man, the DVDs of *The L Word* that I hid under my pillow so that my roommate wouldn't find them, Momma in the Maywood hospital after a bad infection, the cancer spreading throughout her body, the day I received the news that she would soon have to be under hospice care. I think about how, to Father Dore, my gayness is not visible like a tattoo, and I wonder if he can see the rage in my eyes.

I grow bolder in my anger, which makes it easier for me to ask him the following question: "You said earlier that my mother's funeral was really difficult for you. Did it change your relationship to God?" He stares at me for a moment, and he looks puzzled, so I try to clarify. "I mean, are there ever times when you've questioned whether or not God really exists?"

He responds to my question with a story about a parishioner who, after visiting his mother, a late-stage dementia patient in a nursing home, had asked Dore, "Why me?" Dore's response was, "Why not you? Why do you think you're exempt from hardship?" God never promised us that terrible things wouldn't happen, he says, before a loud exhale. But then Dore's tone shifts, becoming softer and more solemn, as he confesses, "I was angry at God when my mother died." He continues, looking down at the floor, "My favorite song from the church used to be 'Be Not Afraid.' The band played it for my 25th anniversary in the church, and also for my 40th anniversary. But then my mom died some years after that, and they played it at her funeral. So I won't listen to it again. Right before she died, she had fear in her eyes.

164

She was very afraid to die."

His own eyes widen as he talks about his mother's fear, and I remember something I'd briefly forgotten about Momma's funeral.

Momma requested all female pallbearers— postmortem feminism. My dad, sisters, and I stood before the church's entrance behind them. Father Dore stood in front of the pallbearers and her casket, but he faced us instead of looking forward toward the altar. The pianist began playing "On Eagle's Wings," and the cantor waited for a cue to start singing the first verse. The music must have played for just about thirty seconds before my dad had to excuse himself to cry in the church bathroom, to the right of where we were standing. When my dad exited the bathroom, his eyes were red. Dore looked at my dad, and as soon as he knew my dad had been crying, he began crying, too. Then my sisters and I cried as we trailed behind Momma's raised casket down the altar while "On Eagle's Wings" played. As we advanced toward the altar, Father Dore was still crying, but he also looked worried, or scared. He seemed unsure.

Now, as he looks straight at me instead of down at the floor, Dore talks more about his own mother's death. He doesn't say more about his anger— just what relieves him of it. "When I'm angry, I find it's best for me to have a routine." His routine involves taking flowers to his mother's grave on the anniversary of her death. "And I just talk to her."

When I look into Father Dore's eyes this time, they don't look rigid or judging like they did when I was in grade school. Instead, they look weary— his eyes remind me of Momma's eyes after her double mastectomy— and like his mother before her death, there is some fear in them.

I said goodbye to Momma in 2007, at the end of August, as my dad got ready to drive me to my college orientation. It was then, as I hugged her, that I realized that she and my dad probably hadn't told me everything. I could feel it in her hug— that no matter the treatment, she was going to die, and the two of them had known that for a while. Momma was not big on physical affection in part because hugs were painful for her, but when we hugged before I loaded my last suitcase into my dad's car, I thought it might never end. She was crying— sobbing, really— and our bodies were shaking as we held each other. She was squeezing me, and it must have been hurting her. I didn't want to leave, but I knew she would never let me stay.

I'd only seen Momma cry once before that, on the day her dad died.

And I only saw her cry once after that, when she was in hospice, high on morphine, and insisting that her dad was there, in her bedroom.

I cried through the two hours it took for my dad to drive to South Bend, even when he stopped at McDonald's to get us McFlurries. When we got to Notre Dame, his alma mater, I asked him if we could just sit on a bench for a while. Because he put his enthusiasm for showing me his favorite parts of campus on the back burner, I knew that he was feeling many of the same things that I was. We sat in silence on that bench together as happy freshmen walked by us with new student IDs around their necks and shower caddies in grocery bags around their wrists.

Referring to God and the stories of the Bible, Dore admits that every once in a while, when he's praying, he thinks to himself, "Is this shit real?" We laugh together, the sincere kind of laughter, and in this moment I realize that Father Dore is not wiser than the rest of society, nor is he otherworldly. He's just trying to figure out how to exist.

A few months after Momma died, I went to a fortuneteller in Oak Park. I hoped she would see a future that I couldn't. After looking at her tarot cards, she told me that she saw a tall, dark man as my future husband, and that I should call my mother more often.

I remember someone saying to me, "I guess even the best doctors couldn't perform a miracle," on the day of Momma's funeral.

I remember my grandma's sister, "a fat Betty Boop," she called herself, as she finished gluing on her fake eyelashes and then sat down to read my palms, her manicured fingers tickling the creases of my skin and her scratchy voice saying, "Well, sweet child, it looks to me like you'll live a long, long time."

I think that losing a parent even at an old age places a person, at least temporarily, back in the role of a neglected, confused child. As I watch Father Dore, I realize that I long for something from God that's impossible for me to get. I want to curl up in a ball and lean my head on God's shoulders while he shushes me and tells me everything will be all right. I want God to sing me to sleep. In the morning I want him to tell me to get up and make my bed. I want him to tell me that I'm irritable because I'm not eating enough, and then I want him to say, "Check the cabinets. I just bought some Rice Krispy Treats." I want him to tell me that he talked to my sisters and my dad and he comforted them, too. I want him to hold our family together. I want him to hear me play the trumpet and tell me that I'm talented and that he's so proud of me.

"You leave your clothes on the floor, you leave your towel on the floor, you leave your books and laptop throughout the house, you are cranky in the morning, you are noisy late at night, yet each time you leave here to return to college, I'm as sad as the first time." That's what I want God to say. "I miss you," I want him to say. "Everything is O.K. You are strong. You are smart. You are beautiful. I'm trying to figure out how to get an AIM screen name so I can iChat with you. Do your homework. Go to class. Stop swearing. Caitlin Hogan Garvey, I am so mad at you. Call and check in when you get to Katie's house. Stop shaving your eyebrows or you'll start to look like Whoopi Goldberg. You really need to get a haircut. Remember to take your vitamins. I love you."

I want God to wear white polo shirts and khakis when it's Sunday before church and he's getting the paper and Krispy Kreme donuts for my sisters and me— he doesn't eat any, he has a grapefruit instead. I want him to cheer too loudly at my swim meet. I want him to visit seven different Hallmarks trying to find the Princess Diana Bear Beanie Baby for my Easter basket. I want him to throw a spoon at me when he's mad at me for something stupid I said. I want him to buy a Halloween costume for our dog.

But it isn't really God that I want at all.

Dedicated to: Rev. Thomas M. Dore, pastor emeritus of St. Giles Parish in Oak Park, who passed away Dec. 17, 2020, at the age of 85.

Shikaakwa *Robert Burkenhare*

Q: How many Chicagoans does it take to change a light bulb?

A: One, but the guy has to have grown up in Bridgeport, have clout with the mayor's office, a cousin who's an alderman, and, if asked, would unironically call Affirmative Action "reverse racism."

Q: The Chicago flag has four stars. What do they represent?
A: Those aren't stars. Those are bullet holes.

Chicago comes from the French who rendered the Native American word *shikaakwa* into *Chicagoua*. That French pronunciation would later be adopted by the band The Fugs in their song "CIA Man" to more closely rhyme Chicago with Nicaragua. The native word means, as every Chicago kid knows, stinking onion.

How is Chicago like an onion? Not in the stink, which is no worse than most cities (have you been to Baltimore?) but in the layers. The center of town contains roads above roads—most famously Wacker Drive with its upper and lower distinctions. Layers may also be found on the Chicago hot dog, each topping (mustard, relish, onions, tomato wedges, pickle spear, sport peppers, celery salt) an indicator of yet another culture coming to the city and adding their flavor to the encased meat. And then there's the deep dish pizza, a layered marvel, though not the true representation of Chicago pizza, but let's not get into all that.

Were one feeling particularly Marxist, they might argue that the layers are evident in the rigid class strata, though I doubt Chicago is different from anywhere else in that regard.

Of course, the whole stinking onion thing is bunk. Recent

scholarship has revealed the true definition of the indigenous word *shikaakwa*: Pretty city with racists.

Old joke: Chicago has two seasons: winter and construction.

True, but if you live in one of the neglected south or west side neighborhoods, substitute "murder" for "construction."

Straight Lines:
1865: Two Chicagoans walk into the Stockyards. (Moo!)
1893: Two Chicagoans walk into the World's Fair. (Eskimos!)
1948: Two Chicagoans walk into a candy factory. (Boom!)
1968: Two Chicagoans walk into Grant Park. (Ouch!)
1974: Two Chicagoans walk into the Sears Tower. (Tall!)
2009: Two Chicagoans walk into the Willis Tower. (Deal with it.)
2020: Two Chicagoans walk into the Loop. (Crickets.)

A Tree Dies in Wrigleyville
Christopher Sebela

For countless people, living and long-dead, Wrigley Field has always loomed large as an iconic landmark. For me, growing up two blocks down from the ballpark, it literally loomed over my life. I could go out and look to where the street ended at a huge wall of the baseball fortress. On game days, I would walk home to the oceanic sound of crowds cheering or the low hiss of several thousand people just existing in a place together. I remember the night the Cubs were headed to the playoffs and how the city went apehouse and crowded around the stadium even though no one was inside playing. Asking my mom if we could go too, she somehow agreed to this idiotic kid suggestion while pretending she had any fondness for the team or the sport.

The Cubs were weaved into the fabric of my early life. Playing outside our apartment and hearing Harry Carey lead the crowd in yet another "Take Me Out to the Ballgame" was as normal as hearing the El train roar past in the distance every few minutes. The windows of all the houses for blocks around— from our working-class street to the rich snobs one block over on Alta Vista Terrace— sprouted yellow signs for the *No Lights At Wrigley Field* campaign, some of which remained for years after the battle was lost. I could always tell when a game was closing by the uptick in pedestrians leaving early to get to their cars, and when it was really over and our street became a parade of people too drunk to walk and too devoted to a team that was hellbent on letting them down.

By all rights, I should be a Cubs fan. One of those obnoxious ones who uses his childhood setting as bragging rights to prove what a much truer and purer fan he is. But that night was the last concrete memory I have of caring about the Cubs. Or baseball. Or Wrigley Field. But not long after that, I wasn't just done with all of it, I wanted to burn it all down.

I was as dumb as any kid, and my opinion of the effect I had on the world was equally stupid. I mention this to explain the summer day I focused all my attention on the tiny sapling that was growing on the "outer lawn"— that median of grass between the sidewalk and the blacktop that doesn't have a name society as a whole agrees on, so I'm giving it one.

Because it was growing in front of our coach house apartment— I could see it from the living room window— the tree became mine somehow. Maybe someone planted it, maybe it wasn't even a tree, but once I claimed it as mine, it became my responsibility to help it become something huge and impossible as all the actual full-grown older versions that lined our street.

Every day I'd fill up the biggest plastic cup we had in the kitchen, walk it down the stairs from our 2nd floor apartment, then up the path that wound around the house that sat in front of ours on the same lot, go out the opening in the fence to the outer lawn and dump the water into the soil at the base of the tree. Sometimes I'd get a refill if it was hot or the sapling looked a little forlorn. I didn't (and mostly still don't) know much about trees, but I knew (and know) they need water like the rest of us. If I didn't provide any, it only seemed natural that it would die.

This tree needed this grade-schooler, and luckily this grade-schooler was a latchkey kid of a single mom and had lots of time after school to water his pet tree.

After one unremarkable game day at Wrigley, a huge crowd poured out and down our street, wobbly and yelling because the Cubs probably blew it again (they did that a lot back then). I always tended to head inside when the rush started, because I always got the sense that anything could pop off with these people at any moment, and I didn't want to be nearby when it did. One of the rare benefits of having an alcoholic dad is you can sense these things like a dowser rod. Once the last few stragglers had gotten done vomiting on the street and found their cars, I went back outside with my big plastic cup of water, happy to do my job turning trees big.

I could see it as soon as I began the walk up from our building. My tree didn't look quite right, it was out of sync from the silhouette I'd etched into my brain. As I got closer, everything pulled into focus and my whole body sagged. The sapling had been violently split apart, torn by drunken human hands into two pieces, each barely able to stand upright. It had been

171

fine an hour ago, so the only explanation that made sense, then and now, was Cubs fans.

Anger's been an issue for me most of my life, but this is one of the earliest moments I can recall that same sort of biblical fury I would access far too often later down the road. I was pissed off and I wanted someone to pay. I wanted whatever drunk jerk that tore my tree apart to be torn apart the same way. I might have cried, which is a feature that still persists to this day as well. Heading inside and telling my mom, she sympathized, but she wasn't surprised.

Maybe a normal person takes that experience in for a day and then moves on, but for me, it fueled an active dislike of Chicago sports. I briefly tried throwing my support to the White Sox instead, but they were even less exciting than the Cubs. The Bears had briefly won my heart and mind with the Super Bowl Shuffle a year or two earlier, but once it became clear that was a one-time only event, I dropped them. I don't even think I knew the Bulls existed; the Chicago Sting and the Blackhawks seemed completely made-up. I had no refuge, so I walked away entirely. But I still had to live in the shadow of Wrigley.

Now when I would hear Harry Carey starting to sing from inside our apartment, I would go outside and yell "Shut up" at the sky. Even the roar of the crowd on the rare occasion of a Cubs player doing something competent would make me mad. I watched the drunken parade of fans go by, not with fear, but disdain. Where walking around outside Wrigley on game days used to be kind of magical, now it was an obstacle course of jerks I had to escape, dead certain that somewhere out there, or inside the park, was the guy who killed my tree.

When the Bulls won their first championship, I briefly allowed myself a bit of excitement. No matter how jaded I'd gotten about sports, even that was powerless in the face of Michael Jordan, but that faded not long after, and when they won a second time, I was back in my bunker built to keep sports out.

And so it went until one summer day, me and a bored friend took a tab of weak LSD and wandered around the Lincoln Park neighborhood where I was living in my first apartment. The drugs came on pretty slow and lazy, so after a few hours I headed home and met up with a different friend of mine, unaware that the Bulls were on the verge of winning another championship. Until the city went apehouse right outside my studio window.

After a while, I suggested to my friend we go out and watch the festivities, so we headed out into the night and watched Chicago celebrating up and down Clark Street, horns honking, flags waving, a whole scene just pouring out of apartments unplanned, forming an event. We sat back and watched and, blessed with the kind of chaos a person on LSD wishes would happen, I felt that fist inside me unfold a bit. But not for long. Because however big all these franchises and dynasties loomed over the city, none of them were ever quite as big as my tree would be now if some asshole fan hadn't destroyed it.

Your Driver Has Arrived
Nestor Gomez

By this time, I had been driving for the ridesharing companies for almost a year.

I made my way late one night to pick up a passenger in Wicker Park. There was a group of about six guys at the exit of a bar. I wondered if my passenger was amongst them.

"I hope he doesn't try to bring the whole group in my car," I told myself. "This ain't no clown car."

My mind drifted back to my first day as a ridesharing driver. I was given a training session by an experienced driver. He told me how to use the application, and to be aware that I will be rated by my passengers on my driver performance. He also warned me to never let too many people ride in my car. "You can get pulled over and get a ticket," he had said. "Let them know they all have to have their seat belts on."

But as a driver, I quickly learned that some people didn't care about safety. Especially drunk people. I had to refuse to start the car until they let some people out, or until they canceled the ride and ordered a bigger vehicle.

Suddenly I heard someone knocking on my car window. It was my passenger. He was alone, but obviously very drunk. As soon as he sat in the back seat, he made a noise as if he was about to puke.

"If someone pukes in your car," the instructor had told me, "make sure to take a picture of them and the damage, so you can charge them the three-hundred-dollar cleaning fee."

I got my phone ready just in case I had to take a picture. But at the last minute, the passenger opened the door and puked on the sidewalk.

The application told me where my passenger was going, but I asked him, just to be sure.

"Always, always, double-check their destination address," my instructor had told me. "Especially if they're drunk. You don't want to drive them to the wrong place, and then have them blame you for it."

"Ah ha, ah ha," my passenger said as an affirmation. I started driving. Soon I heard him snoring in the back seat.

"If your passenger ever falls sleep," my instructor had told me, "don't take them for a longer ride than they need. They can always check the route you took in their application the next day."

"And how do I wake them up?" I had asked. "Can I shake them, or poke them?"

"Only if you want to be sued," he had answered. "You just have to talk to them and give them a few minutes to wake up."

But I had been driving for a while now, and I knew that talking never woke the drunk, sleeping passengers. So as I got my drunk passenger to his destination in Pilsen, I parked the car, turned my radio on, and raised the volume all the way up. The passenger sat up and looked around a bit, confused.

"We're here," I said. I thought that if my instructor could see me now, he would be so proud of me.

Just then, my passenger got out of my car into the cold winter air. He took a few drunken steps and fell face-first into a bank of snow on the sidewalk.

My first instinct was to drive away.

"You're not supposed to touch them," I heard myself thinking as I got out of my car to help the guy. Against my better judgment, I grabbed him by his coat and helped him up. He leaned against my body to keep from falling.

"That thing you did with the radio to wake me up," he said. "That was a nice trick."

"What are you talking about?" I asked.

"I didn't teach you that," he said, with a drunk smile.

I looked at him in shock.

"Don't you recognize me?" he asked. "I'm your instructor."

It was true.

"I got to tell you," he added. "You have come a long way."

"Thanks," I said. "But let's worry about you now. Can you make it

175

all the way to your house?"

He shook his head no. So I helped him get to his door. I stood there as he tried in vain to use his keys. Finally, I took the keys from him and opened the door myself. The door opened to a flight of stairs.

"I live on the second floor," he said. "But I don't think I can make the stairs on my own."

He leaned heavily on me as I helped him up the stairs. This time he didn't even try to open the door, he just looked at me. So I opened the door, put the keys in his coat pocket, and pushed him inside the apartment. Maybe I pushed him a little bit too hard, because he fell face-first in the middle of the living room.

I closed the door and ran back to my car.

The next day, I checked my phone to see how much money I had made driving the night before. There was an email. It was from my instructor, praising me as a driver. He didn't mention the fact that he had been drunk and fallen in the snow, but he ended by stating that the student had surpassed the teacher.

And I told myself, "You are right about that."

American Sfumato   *Vojislav Pejović*

Miloš's head is buzzing as he keeps thinking, or murmuring, who knows, something about air-conditioned rooms without windows; then about the neon lamps, brains, rats, and the tang of chemicals. After that: the hippocampi and the sea horses, the sea and the horses, cold war, cold sandwiches, cold fingers, hot palms, steamy thighs, the winter, the summer. Once more, for sure, he ponders the rats. Then, for a while, only the frost bites.

How did I get here, how the hell did I get here, laments Miloš under his breath, as a swarm of icicles gathers on his scarf and as his eyes start adjusting to darkness. Came by night, leaving by night, he keeps saying to himself, and then almost shouts: fuck this cold, I just can't get used to it, can't get used to the fucking fifteen below (Celsius) or five above (Fahrenheit), can't get used to the fucking Fahrenheit scale. Then his mental screen flickers once more with images of the windowless room, third door from the left, at the Biochemistry Department: the one he just abandoned, with a feeling of a massive, thorny crystal forming in his stomach. And it's only been a couple of weeks since he phoned back home: I did it, I became an Assistant Professor! Father was in Crmnica, paying his dues at the Wine and Bleak Festival, or in his case, The Festival of Wine & Wine. Fish is for the pussy cats, I need somethin' that kicks ass, he roared, intoxicated, through the long-distance connection. I need somethin' that kicks aaaaasss, echoed the choir of his drinking buddies; hey, ya motherfuckers, did ya hear that: Miloš has become a professa!

After twenty minutes or so of braving the ice and the freezing wind, during which he masterfully managed—not once, but three times—to avoid an abrupt encounter of his nose, bottom, back with the petrified snow, Miloš finally reaches the three-floor apartment building that has been his residence since the past July. On the facade, only two windows are illuminated: in one he can make out Kate, already in her new coat, staring into a frigid, streetlight-suffused darkness; the other is visited by Camille, briefly, but long enough for Miloš to realize that she opted for a miniskirt in this bitching cold weather. I'm late, I'm going to be late, how the hell did I get into this, he grumbles to himself, unwrapping the scarf, sprinting up a few flights of stairs.

Hey hon, you late, you late, and you know it's not Halloween, says Kate in her broken Serbian, pressing her warm cheek and lips to the general area of his face, anesthetized with cold, and then moves on, direction bathroom, carrying a grinning, bare-bottomed child over her shoulder. Hi, Mr. Milosh, says Camille, passing by equally fast, but without a kiss, alas, without a kiss, holding an equally grinning child, and you know, she adds, it's a good look for you, and releases her curt, almost shrill giggle. Miloš then makes a step toward a mirror, where he meets a puzzled, pale, half-frozen creature, someone who looks like him, for sure, but otherwise a strange fellow, someone who put on his puffed-up down jacket over a blood-stained lab coat, which makes him look quite unconventional, like a ragged clown on the verge of tears (I'd say), or even a resident of some restricted-access institution, one of the more reliable sort, someone who handled his drug regimen well and was allowed to take public transportation home for the weekend. Miloš's cheeks are still burning with cold, and his brain feels a little numb, too, which is why he can't even blush, or come up with some witty or meaningful reason for choosing such attire. It's very sad, he thinks, that the first thing that comes to mind is a scatterbrained-scientist cliché, sad indeed, because that's the cliché he despises above all others, as he gets rid of the jacket, since he hasn't, no, he has never been scatterbrained, or even distracted, crumbling up his lab coat and jamming it into his backpack, it's only that he's overworked, because, he zips up the backpack, for years now he goes to work by night and returns by night, and thinks hey, idiot, you're gonna be late, as he conjures with anger, with bouts of disgust, the image of himself in that accidental costume of his, a costume, he starts to believe, that gives him away so mercilessly, as only costumes are capable of doing.

Then he too heads for the bathroom, where Kate is about to finish her brief makeup routine, and where Camille, kneeling by the bathtub, oversees Sasha and Sophie in their bubble bath universe. It's easy to make fun of the working class, tries Miloš as easy-goingly as he can and grabs his toothbrush, the tip of which, he never fails to recall as he switches it on, can reach up to thirty thousand super-brief jerks per minute. *I know you're glad to see us, hon*, protests Kate, again in broken Serbian, *but you know we have two bathroom*, upon which Miloš shrugs and grins with his mouth full of foam, which, stirred up by the turbo-speedy bristles, sprays everywhere around, especially over an arm of Kate's new coat. Kate releases a theatrical growl, because she only rarely loses her cool, and leaves the bathroom in haste, upon which Miloš locks his lips tight and lowers his gaze to Camille, whose perfect, muscular legs now lie folded underneath her red-green tartan skirt. She looks at him coyly, like an accomplice, like someone who's having lots of fun, and he has serious trouble keeping his eyes on hers, the color of ripe blackberries, because just a chin below opens up a path into the depths of her radiating bosom, across which his children have already cast luminescent handfuls of the bathing bubbles.

Have fun, you guys, and don't worry about them, chirps Camille in her happy soprano, while Miloš and Kate, withdrawing to the door, apply exploding kisses to the twins' enormous cheeks. At the sight of their parents disappearing, the children release *mamadadaaa* in unison and start advancing across the living room. Camille has to react fast, because Sasha and Sophie, as she knows too well, ignore the fact that they started walking only a month ago, and hurl themselves and stumble and run into furniture edges with their soft temples and foreheads. In the bustle that ensues, Miloš manages to anchor one thorough look into the depths of Camille's inviting cleavage, and maybe he would have stayed that way had Kate not pulled at his arm and said, c'mon, let's go already.

In the frozen seats of their car, adjusting their minds to silence, fearing that they'll hear screams of brain-injured children, Miloš and Kate manage to exchange their first intimate glances of the day. Our first date in six months, says Kate and turns the key, waking up the engine of their white Honda Civic. And she also says: *if we're late for the movie, honey, I swear, I kill you.* Miloš is sick of the cold, of almost solidified breath that's leaving his nostrils, and says sorry, it was a complete madness at work, Dmitri and Ken were exchanging their childhood stories, so they missed their turn for the ultracentrifuge, but see, we're on time, we're so lucky that we've found Camille. *Hon, if you don't stop talk about lab, I also kill you*, replies Kate, looking at him askance, smiling with the corners of her mouth, and moving her index finger, in lieu of a knife, across her muscular, elongated neck.

179

Miloš welcomes the fact that Kate decided to drive: he hopes to be able to focus, to round up his thoughts, to redirect them, no, to blow them away by some unexpected cortical winds, to expel them everywhere, without mercy, actually to stop thinking at all, neon lamps, windowless rooms, to halt the pestilent brain, let Dmitri and Ken now have their fun in the centrifuge room until three in the morning, let them compare their childhood stories all they want, a suburb of Saint Louis and the very downtown of Dniepropetrovsk; luckily, one can at least count on Wei-Chen, he's the only one who has no desire to recollect sad and funny tales of his childhood, although, truth be told, he did tell him once about the long-gone days, about his father the colonel and growing up in the garrisons, about the frozen steppe by the Mongolian border and the holes in the ground for the prisoners of war. As Miloš tries to rein himself in, Kate examines herself for a moment in the rearview mirror and, before shifting into drive, takes off her gloves, rubs her palms against each other with considerable fervor, and presses them, almost ignited, to Miloš's hurting earlobes.

The Honda already feels like a small Japanese oven, the heat suffocates Miloš's cerebral storms, and he finds it harder and harder to spin the thoughts of rats, hippocampi, American-Ukranian friendship, and Chinese-Mongolian deserts. Kate also senses that the turbulences in his head are winding down, and her thin and forceful fingers, endowed with an impeccable timing—something that, it has to be said, Miloš always appreciated greatly—abandon the stick shift for a second and clasp themselves around Miloš's unsuspecting quadriceps. Hon, don't sleep, she says, *I'm so curious, email says that Todd Haynes will come maybe, he once was in our college, and it was great.*

How to handle the latest Todd Haynes movie? *Far From Heaven*, he recalls, was unbearable; he simply can't get the Americans' obsession with the fifties, as far as he's concerned the most boring decade in the history of decades. As if reading his thoughts, Kate says you may actually like this one, and with a short, vague announcement (for which one can be grateful), puts in a CD that Miloš can't make out in the darkness, nor does he hear what else Kate has to say, since the car has reached the shoreline curve of Sheridan Road. It's pitch dark and the lake is invisible, but Miloš knows it's there, omnipresent, with its lid of thick ice and snow, the anti-Adriatic, fish-infested steppe, a sight that always left him breathless. Then there's a guitar, the murmur of the crowd, the nasal voice of a young man in his very famous song; then the applause.

The Honda Tropic rushes down Lake Shore Drive; the night is cloudless and still, only a stray car here and there, Chicago's North Side on their right, and on their left the enormous lake, stiff with cold. Kate's mood improves by the minute, she says I know you'll have fun, Cate Blanchett's in it, and so's Charlotte Gainsbourg, but Miloš has checked out for a while, his forehead pressed against the window, sleighed far into the lake, the anti-Adriatic, maybe the Adriatic Sea itself. Kate places her hand on Miloš's thigh one more time, and, after fifteen or so minutes filled mostly with small, unrelated words, the two of them sail onto the rooftop of a garage. The sudden silence of the extinguished engine startles them both, interrupting Kate's inner musings about the movie, Miloš, and the passage of time, as well as Miloš's fantasies involving large bodies of water, and for a second or two the car is devoid of a single word or thought, until someone says, it's not exactly clear who, I can't believe it, honey, our first date in six months. Then they leave the vehicle—which has already started succumbing to the cold—examine the surroundings as if checking for surveillance, and then, hand in hand, enter a shopping-mall-slash-movie-theater.

Judging by the crowd around the cash registers, there are quite a few people anxious to see Todd in person. Miloš frowns, suppressing the ever stronger need to grumble, but Kate, who loses her cool very rarely indeed, reaches into her coat and takes out two pre-purchased tickets: the wonderful, reliable Kate, so unwilling to allow overcrowded cash registers to spoil anything. Hey, look over there, it's Amy and Pete, she exclaims, pointing at a couple waiting for the tickets, upon which Miloš says great, I'll be right back, I need to get one, you know I have to. I know, shame on you, she says, *prior vegetarian; I want one too, with many mustard.*

Carrying them both in one hand, two inviting, foot-long hot dogs, adorned with rich applications of mustard squeezed out of an oversized plastic trough with a pump, and holding, in his other hand, a huge styrofoam cup full of sparkling diet Coke—almost an entire liter: the portion that he and Kate go through when in the movies, fighting for the same thick straw—Miloš manages to maintain his balance through the crowd and locate his wife. It's still not quite clear, he learns, whether Mr. Haynes is going to show up; he also learns that Amy too remembers his visit to the Modern Culture and Media Department at Brown. For some inexplicable reason, Miloš is convinced that Todd will stand them up, but he keeps that uncomfortable thought to himself, feeling just fine, listening to a very musical duelling of smarts between Amy and his wife, bringing the lukewarm hotdog to his mouth, exchanging a glance or two with Pete, who also did not go to an Ivy League school, and then says Pete, my fwiend, sowwy, thif hot dog isfo good, did you watch Fav From Heaven, how did you wike it, and Pete says no, I didn't. Then it's Pete's turn to say something: Miloš is chewing, listening politely, no, he on the other hand did not see that one, and then, noticing that people are slowly flocking in, wraps one arm under Kate's—while holding, in the other, with a great deal of effort, the bottom of the enormous cup and his partly finished hot dog—and starts pleading that they enter before all the good seats are taken.

We apologize, but Mr. Haynes won't be able to greet you this evening, says a young man, stepping bravely in front of the audience and asking for silence, which forms only briefly and then dissolves into a faint sigh of disappointment, followed by a reluctant applause when Mr. Haynes's latest movie finally begins. Miloš can't say that he really understands what it is about, other than Bob Dylan, incarnated by several men and the divine Cate Blanchett, and that's okay, he thinks, since he kinda always liked his music, but above all the lyrics: catenating images, troubadouring rhymes, women, history, social injustice, then women again. There he is, a black boy who's Bob Dylan, riding a freight car through some America. He's surrounded by hobos, bad intentions are on their faces, like when they take away his guitar case, on which it says THIS MACHINE KILLS FASCISTS. Those exact words were on Guthrie's guitar, says Kate in her softest cinema whisper, and the boy jumps out of the train to save his dear life, life of a fascist-killer, and plunges into an icy, greenish river, where he's swallowed by a great white whale.

An hour or so into the movie, diet Coke finds its way through Miloš's system and he needs to leave his seat for a moment. As he urinates, it seems, three or four minutes at least, with a feeling of doing it in a Todd Haynes' bathroom, he realizes that he'll have to admit to Kate, because fair is fair, that this movie is quite compelling. Then, as he rushes back to his seat, men's and women's rooms open simultaneously (Miloš swears that's how it happened), and he almost collides with a dark-haired woman wearing a short black dress. Miloš's eyes skip over her features (Asian, petite, beauty mark at the tip of her left eyebrow), and his heart leaps and his diaphragm starts trembling, pulling along the entire abdomen. Excuse me, she says, passing him by, leaving a vanishing cloud of fragrance in her wake, which makes Miloš's innards go absolutely crazy, and he pulls at her arm and asks, Kumiko, is that you?

I beg your pardon, says the pretty Asian, I'm sorry, he retorts clumsily, don't you remember me, it's Milosh, from Kotor, nineteen-ninety-four. She smiles, she wears a lot of makeup, maybe it's not Kumiko after all, because this girl readily says, sorry, it must've been someone else. Have you ever been in Kotor, Montenegro, Adriatic coast, he goes on, stubbornly, but she just shakes her head, that must've been someone else, repeats, and glides back into darkness.

Sorry, it's all that Coke, Miloš says to Kate, taking her warm and bony hand, as Cate Blanchett Dylan rolls down some English lawns with the Fab Four. Aided by the greenish reflections from the screen, Miloš manages to locate a female silhouette devoid of sharp features, three rows in front of him, and he's dead certain that it's her.

It was the summer of ninety-four, almost the climax of Yugoslav wars, and that's something that Miloš doesn't like to talk about, something he even hasn't told Kate, who at the time was deep in subjects that were taught at Brown University's Department for Modern Culture and Media, passing her days without a slightest notion that there was a Miloš, who was spending that summer, like most others, in his aunt's house for rent in the coastal town of Kotor. During winter, the aunt was a florist and a state oil company employee on permanent furlough; during summer, she rented rooms of her semi-dilapidated villa to whomever and for whatever price, because the times were ugly, and no one had any money, and there was happiness with no end when some Americans showed up and said that they needed room and board.

Miloš can't recall exactly what it was that they were doing in Kotor, those Americans, each one occupying a room in The Flower, the town's foremost bed and breakfast. He remembers that it had to do with the war, peace, understanding among peoples, but also that none of that mattered at all, since the situation was developing beyond all expectations: already on day three, he was sniffing fresh sweat from the nape of her neck, while the indolent air from the bay was breezing in slowly, and the sun was taking its time to emerge above the steep mountains, as if reluctant to shine on the world in which everything, finally, was as it should be. On day five, he rented a boat and they went to Perast, where they pressed their bodies together on the mosaic floor of a roofless sixteenth century palace, while on day six they took to the open sea, so that Kumiko could set foot on that wondrous beach, which, ages ago, before there was tap water and asphalt road, was rumored to be the only pristine cove on the Adriatic coast. Alas, they were chased away, by men with thick skulls, black guns, and fat racing boats, so they returned to auntie's *pensione* and made love with fortitude and sadness, until the sun came up one more time, until they both collapsed with exhaustion.

In the early afternoon of the seventh day, while Miloš was procuring food for The Flower, the Americans packed up their stuff and vanished: without an announcement, forwarding address, or farewell letter. Auntie just shrugged, went once more with her index finger over a tiny roll of US dollars, and shuffled away to clean the emptied rooms. Miloš searched everywhere he could: along the coast, in Podgorica, even Belgrade, and then decided to follow his father's example and drown himself in wine & wine. He was not his father, though: by next summer he sobered up, shaved off his freshly grown bohemian beard, and managed to enroll in a Neuroscience PhD program in Chicago. He knew her name, body, and the complex topology of her scents, and that he needs to do his absolute best to find her.

The years that went by turned Kumiko into a queasy memory, one to which, we can only assume, Miloš occasionally masturbates with sadness. Women, and everything else he yearned for, marched through his life in a sufficient quantity, so when one day he saw Kate, standing in line for the latest movie by Pedro Almodóvar, he could finally be sure that what was driving him was not hunger, or despair, or the pointless need to forget (what? and whom?), but the pursuit of happiness, so precious and so simple. Had he succeeded in tracking down Kumiko, he was sure, it would have ended very badly, just as badly as it now ends between Charlotte Gainsbourg and Bob Dylan, played on this occasion by Heath Ledger.

The real Dylan finally appears, blowing a solo in his most famous song; the closing credits roll, Sonic Youth start singing I'm not there, I'm gone. Kate stretches in her seat, enthralled, with her eyes moist, with the exact same look Miloš saw after the manly Marco and the beautiful Alicia—in the fateful Almodóvar movie—exchanged glances at the end of a show in which everyone, Marco and Alicia, Miloš and Kate, would be awakened from the domesticated horrors of their everyday existence by a ballet piece with a happy finale. The audience leave their seats, a few enthusiasts clap, careless feet trample over crumpled popcorn bags. Miloš can't resist and looks around, but the Japanese girl with a lot of makeup is nowhere to be found. Sure it's better this way, a thought zaps through his head, and he too shakes hands with Pete and Amy and says goodbye guys, it was great to see you.

At the garage rooftop, while scanning their surroundings (because a night like this, in which hands are held atop an immense, winter-riddled city, is almost mystical and deserving of special attention), Miloš grabs Kate around the waist, draws her near, and nails his manly smooch on her grinning mouth. Happy birthday, he says, and produces out of nowhere a tiny faux-mahogany box. What's this, asks Kate, who likes surprises after all, but Miloš stays mum and lets the moment unfold, in which Kate lifts the lid of the heavy little box and discovers a pair of tar-black trilobites, curled up in obedient repose, conjoined with the light-gray limestone in which they were fossilized, and at least, this Miloš says out loud, at least five hundred million years old. Kate's laughter bursts among the rooftops, and that's how this story could end.

The story, however, does not end that way. We know for certain that, after Kate's petite happiness explosion, the two of them got into their white Honda Civic, turned up the heat, and put in the *I'm Not There* soundtrack, purchased immediately after the movie. At about the same moment the car reached the empty Lake Shore Drive, Jim James & Calexico began their moaning version of "Goin' to Acapulco," Kate, with her lips tightly pressed together, released a stream of silent tears on the collar of her new coat, and Miloš, yet again, went sailing the vast memory expanses. After she parked in front of the apartment, Kate asked out loud, in a voice tamed and upbeat, whether Sasha and Sophie are asleep, and Miloš, we can be pretty sure, seized a moment to conjure an image of Camille, of her warm bosom and her deep-dark eyes. At the end of that very long day, chances are that Kate and Miloš fell asleep in each other's arms, with their limbs tangled up and glistening with sweat, like a couple of trilobites that copulate readily and swiftly, as if sensing the limestone boulder, a bed of chalk in which they'll remain curled up for the next five hundred million years.

Hey, Mr. Tambourine Man, won't you please emerge, come for once out of your troubadouring fog, screw visions, women, and social injustice, and please, please, play a ballad just for me. Play me of the days that hang like drops of honey, of ten-fingered fists of heartbroken lovers, of longing that blows up windbags of one's chest, of giggles and tears and bones and best intentions. Then make a mention of the rugged clown (of me, as I am, as I'm writing this), wrapped up in russets, mottle and moth-bitten, of yearning that makes his skin sore and scarlet, of pathetic gifts for which he is ready (Dylan, Brown, concert—all the best, my dear), weariness of silence, weariness to talk, weariness to scrape away this powdered chalk.

The Art of Persuasion
RL Gehringer

By age thirteen I could talk anyone into anything.

If I needed smokes, I could talk you into raiding your mom's purse or your dad's pack, even if you didn't smoke. If we were a buck two-eighty short for that iguana at Animal Kingdom, I could talk a dozen customers into helping us out. If I felt like cutting school and shooting hoop, I could talk you *and* your little brother into taking the day with me. But I'll tell you when I finally stopped talking people into doing things they didn't really want to do. It was after I talked Roman Matuszak into going snake hunting.

Roman never cared for snakes. Roman cared only for Candy Campanelli. Every morning he waited for Candy's dad to leave for work and her mom to plop on the couch for her morning game shows and afternoon soaps. Candy's mom loved daytime TV so much, she never noticed the two love birds tiptoeing into Candy's room.

"Come on, Roman," I said. "I'll have you back before The Price Is Right."

There was rumor of a bull snake living along the railroad tracks. The reptile had been spotted at the freight yard, under an Anheuser Busch beer train, and in the prairie behind the paper plant. I doubted the existence of this mythical six-foot monster living among our two and three-foot garter snakes. But if there was such a beast, it had arrived by train. "Poor thing hitched a ride here, Roman. He either crawled up inside an open boxcar or found a crevice underneath the car. Either way, it's up to us to save him."

"Sorry, Billy. No can do," Roman said.

"Here," I said, tapping a pocket-sized *"Snakes of the Midwest."* I jammed the book under Roman's nose. "Read this. And have some damn compassion, Roman."

```
Chicago's bull snake population did not
survive its growth. The last bull snake in
Chicago was killed by Ida Templeton on July
3, 1919.
```

Today was July 3, 1969, fifty years to the day.

I slid the book back in my pocket and stood toe-to-toe with my friend. My nose rose only to his chest, the very reason I'd chosen Roman for this mission. At fourteen, six-one and one hundred sixty pounds, Roman Matuszak was older, bigger and tougher than me. He was also better looking. Roman boasted a strong, square jaw, Arctic white teeth—straight and shiny as a fresh-painted windowsill—and something all the girls liked, blue eyes under black hair. Roman needed only a dab of Brylcreem to get that slicked-back style with the floating wave up top. My own hair was dirty brown and dry as straw. No amount of grease could keep it from hanging down across my forehead like a dooper. Greasers v. Doopers. Our whole world was split down that divide. I dressed perfect grease, yet looked like the biggest dooper in Doopersville.

"Well?" I said. "You gonna help me?"

"I'll give you ninety minutes and not one more," Roman said.

We scaled the coal yard fence and came to the barbed wire, diabolically thread through a V shaped brace that flared towards us on the way up and away from us on the way down. Getting your legs over that V shaped brace was treacherous, but Roman and I had come prepared. We wore Straws, black, ultra-light summer shoes with nylon mesh tops and thin rubber soles. Straws kept your feet cool in Chicago's heat and humidity, were perfect for wriggling toes inside tight metal fence holes, and the flexible soles provided balance when squatting atop wobbly barbed wire.

"Ready?" Roman said, as we swayed in the wind.

We leapt like frogs off a riverbank, hit the embankment below the crest of the hill, scrambled up onto the tracks and walked southwest. At Kedzie Avenue an iron viaduct marked our entry into the happiest place on earth.

Avondale Freight Yard. If there was a heaven, this place was it. The yard housed box and hopper cars from across the American heartland, and liberating the contents of those cars was our birthright. Once Roman and I became high school sophomores we'd join our older brothers in this noble neighborhood tradition, including monthly hits on the beer trains. But for now, Avondale Freight Yard was merely our place for cutting school and catching snakes, smoking cigarettes and playing poker, paging through stolen Playboys and watching teenage rumbles from afar. It was our refuge, our wilderness in the heart of the city, a place to conjure the snake gods, brag boldly and dream big.

Halfway through the yard, we came to the beer trains.

"I'm going under to see if he's here." I handed Roman the pillowcase I'd brought for the snake. Roman took it, but he looked bad. Sick, like he was gonna puke.

I'd never realized how truly fearful Roman became at the mere possibility of encountering a snake, but now I saw that he was starting to panic. Roman was the church mouse trembling before the broom. His entire body shook, nose to toes. I grabbed the lower flange of the box car and stopped to provide emotional support. "Roman, if you see the snake, don't try to catch him. Just shout and I'll come get him."

"Don't worry, asshole, I ain't catching no goddamned snake."

I slipped under the car and got down on all fours. The morning was hot and humid, but still cool and dry under the train. I crept along on all fours, sharp little railroad rocks stabbing my palms and knees. Seeing no snakes, I crawled out from under the train.

One look at Roman made me want to crawl back.

"Someone's at the prairie," he said.

"Shit. What's he look like?"

"Like Goblin." Roman's voice wavered

"Gobs ain't no match for you, Roman."

"Screw you, Billy! I ain't fighting that lunatic."

This would have been a good time to back off. But with Goblin

189

around I was more worried about the snake than about Roman.

"Wait. You're afraid of Goblin? How old are you Roman, nine? My God, you're taller. You outweigh him. And you've got a foot of reach on the guy."

Roman's brow furrowed. His expression bounced between courage and fear.

"Besides, you're a *way* better athlete."

Roman smiled. "I am, you know. *Way* better."

He'd mimicked my words. Time to bring it home.

"Hell yeah! Gobs swings with his arms. He's batting what? Two-twenty? The guy pops up everything. What are you batting, Roman? Three eighty? Three eighty-five?"

Roman's eyes sparkled. I lowered my voice to a soft, conspiratorial balloon. "Help me catch this snake and I'll tell Candy how you saved a persecuted creature from certain torture and death at the hands of Gobfucker."

Roman bent to pick up a loose railroad spike. Smiling, he bumped his wrist up and down, enjoying the weight of the object in his palm. While slipping it in his pocket he fingered the point through the fabric of his pants. "Okay. Let's go," he said.

It came that easy. This ability to persuade. I was a year younger and way shorter than my classmates, a decent athlete but a weak fighter. My small stature got me a pass from the big guys, but there'd be no passes in high school, just two months away. That's why I had a stack of library books about persuasion, debate and negotiation. And those books were working. To keep Roman on task I'd applied Shame, Confidence, Pride, Vision and Reward.

And now it was bugging the shit out of me. Because Roman wasn't really a tough guy. Oh, he was big. And he could fight. But he was a puppy. The guy was afraid of snakes for Christ's sakes. In our neighborhood, big guys were hounded even more than little guys. Yet, I can't say I gave Roman's reality any consideration. And now I'd manipulated him into a possible showdown with a known neighborhood terror.

We made our way toward the prairie, keeping one eye open for assholes and our good eyes open for Gobs. Stepping off the embankment, I saw a garter snake weaving through the brush. It wasn't the bull snake we'd come for, but it was huge and I took after it. The snake turned up a slope, gravity slowing his progress. I grabbed the middle of his body. He roiled against capture, muscles pulsing like a bomb in my hands. The angry serpent bent backwards and struck, splitting the skin on my wrist like Eve splitting the skin of an apple. That's when three kids emerged from an underground fort.

"Billy!" Roman yelled, but it was too late. I heard a scruff in the dirt and watched a dust cloud rise, felt the inside crease of a greasy elbow clamp my head. The elbow twisted and the snake slipped from my grasp as my back slammed rocky ground.

Frankie Finnegan's fist hovered over my eye. "Gottcha," he said, yanking me to my feet by the strap of my dago-tee, holding me up like a guy showing off a fish.

I looked at Roman and knew there was no escape. We were victims of the ongoing war between neighborhoods, our fates in the iron fists of Frankie Finnegan, Joey Lester and Helter-Skelter, who everyone just called Skelter.

Cars flashed reflected sunlight on Kimball Avenue. To the adults inside, we were five friends, identical in our baggy grays, black leather belts and white dago-tees. Yet, where we wore Straws, they wore combat boots, and thus the difference. Roman and I dressed for style. Frankie and crew dressed for war.

They'd dug an underground fort into a hill that sloped up towards the tracks. The entrance was hidden behind plywood and branches; no one would ever find our bodies once they got us inside.

Joey pushed me toward their lair. "Move it," he said. Skelter poked Roman with a mop handle he'd whittled into a spear. The smell of wet earth, like a fresh grave, greeted our entrance. Frankie pointed, and his goons marched us to the far wall.

Their bastion was impressive. Slabs of cardboard fortified the mud floor and walls. There were candles and flashlights for card and dice games, and pop bottles—some empty, some still full—were racked like bowling pins in a corner. I knew stolen pop when I saw it and wanted one badly, my throat dry as dust.

Frankie was medium height and skinny, but hard as cement. He had tensile strength, like his body was made from cable wire. Joey Lester was a powerhouse. He worked out in a Belmont Avenue garage and was said to bench-press twice his weight. Skelter was tall and bony. His shoulders stuck out like planks of wood, fingers so long and thin they looked like raw cartilage. Compared to these guys, we were Pillsbury Doughboys.

"Whatchu two got on you?" Frankie said, as Joey rifled our pockets.

Skelter, four inches taller than Roman, towered over us, smacking his fist into a butter-soft Nokona first baseman's glove. This was the glove that had made Skelter's reputation, after he one-punched a guy on the Kedzie bus, then gently slipped the glove from the unconscious man's hand.

"Take it all, Joe." Frankie instructed.

Before leaving home, I'd swiped a Kool Filter King from my mom's pack. Once in the alley, I stuck it behind my ear. Joey plucked it, then tossed it onto the card table.

Four beats. That's how long Skelter waited between smacks in the pocket of his glove. Four beats—the loud, cracking slaps rang off the fort walls like a death knell.

A mile-long train of gruesome scenarios pulled into my brain's freight yard. Murder. Strangulation. Castration. Knives. Fists. Mop handle spears. Frankie looked over at his boys and I saw the judge's gavel striking down, the thumb and forefinger gun, the silent knife across the unsuspecting throat.

"Why you got a pillowcase?" Skelter speared Roman lightly in the ribs.

"Answer the man, Romeo." Joey said.

"It's a keepsake," Frankie offered. "Candy hands 'em out to all the guys."

"It's to mop up his premature loads." Skelter laughed at his own wit and poked Roman's fly. Roman jammed both hands over his middle and bowed to protect himself. Joey guffawed, bowed and covered his own crotch, head bobbing on a double wide neck.

"It's mine," I said. "We're catching garter snakes."

That's when Goblin stuck his nose in the fort.

"You're looking for that bull snake, ain't you?" Gobs directed the question at me, ignoring Frankie and crew in their own house. Frankie's eyes narrowed. Skelter and Joey signaled Frankie with nods light as blinks.

"I saw you come over the tracks," Goblin said, again looking directly at me. Finally, Goblin acknowledged Frankie. By snorting, leaning forward and dropping a thick yellow gob—the kind he was named for—on the cardboard floor.

Frankie eyed the wobbly mound. His eyes mere slits, mouth a closed zipper.

"You're after that bull snake," Goblin repeated the accusation.

"What bull snake?" Frankie said.

Goblin laughed and shook his head pitifully, silently calling Frankie a feeb.

"Beat it, Goblin," Skelter said, "this ain't your party."

"Party? This a party? Well hell then, let's party!"

Gobs took two steps further in. He was almost within punching distance when Skelter jerked forward, one fist in the Nokona, the other ready with the mop handle. Gobs ignored the physical threat and reached a hand around to the back pocket of his baggy grays. The other hand dropped into a front pocket. The hands returned with a two-foot string of firecrackers and a Zippo lighter. Gobs wristed the Zippo open and sparked the flint wheel. The lighter reeked of fluid, and the flame shot six inches high.

"Don't do it, asshole! Don't you fucking do it!" Skelter flexed and snarled, but this time he took a step back. And flung the mop handle at Goblin's head.

Goblin ducked and the spear whizzed past his ear. It bounced off the cardboard wall and rolled. Frankie lunged for the weapon, but Goblin spanked it away with his heel.

A nefarious grin broke under Goblin's nose; his gray eyes gleamed.

Four beats….and Goblin married wick to flame. Four beats….and with a flip of the wrist, Goblin Frisbee-whipped the sizzling firecracker string at Skelter's face. A hundred crackers exploded midair, their snaps and pops erratic like small arms fire. The explosions gained speed until the bursts were a machine gun: *Ratta-tat!-tat!-tat!-tat!*

Skelter covered his face with the Nokona, but the cracker string smartly wrapped around his forearm as if Goblin had willed it. Flashes of yellow and orange burst like exploding birds, and a slithering smoke-Medusa rose from Skelter's hair.

Skelter wrenched like a man possessed, slapping his arm with his free hand until crackers and glove dislodged together. Everything landed at his feet, and now sparks flew up inside Skelter's pant legs, frying the skin above his combat boots. Goblin howled in delight as Skelter wriggled and leapt, shaking out his legs, hopping like a barefoot boy on barbed wire, kicking at the crackers.

One of those kicks sent the Nokona sailing through the fort.

Goblin was a hundred yards away when we got through the exit and bent to catch our breath. On our way out, I'd grabbed my Kool Filter King off the card table and stuck it behind my ear. I expected Joey to notice and take it back, but he and Skelter were staring at Roman's shoe like there was a dead baby under the sole. In the rush to exit, Roman's Straw got tangled in the webbing of Skelter's glove. The legendary, butter-soft, Nokona. Lucky glove. Blessed glove. Glove that had brought Skelter all of his good fortune, in baseball and in life. Skelter leaned forward. "Step on my Nokona, Romeo?"

Roman looked down, shocked to see his Straw mangling the inside leather of Skelter's glove, the outside leather mud-streaked and pebble-pocked.

Roman went for the railroad spike. It wasn't there. He was still patting his pockets looking confused when Joey passed the spike to Skelter.

Skelter waded in—fists like bone-hammers—the spike across the meat of his palm, business end sticking out the pinkie finger side of his curled knuckles.

Roman tried to cover up, but Skelter was quick. He threw a right with a curve ball's snap at the point of contact. The spike caught Roman on the cheekbone and bounced down his face, banging off his upper lip with a loud crunch.

Roman turned his back to Skelter, cupped his hands and spit. A river of blood flowed into his open palms. The blood pooled, then drained through the cracks and there was Roman's front tooth—white as a windowsill—where his hands came together.

Skelter sauntered in for Round II. "That's enough," I said, getting between them. Skelter backed off, don't ask me why. Roman shook his leg and the glove dislodged.

"You two, get gone," Frankie said.

"Leave, before we waste your ass," Joey Lester added.

Roman put the tooth in his pocket and covered the wound with his other hand.

We walked back quickly. Yet once inside the freight yard I somehow convinced my friend to monkey up to the top of a caboose. There was nothing anybody could do for Roman now, might as well relax and enjoy a smoke.

We sat on top of the car but didn't say much. Roman spit blood and ran his fingers over the swollen cheek and busted lip, while I made a ritual of my Kool Filter King.

"How bad is it?" he asked.

"Stiches bad," I said.

"Guess I won't be making out with Candy for a while—if ever."

"You need a dentist, Roman. The girlfriend can wait."

I crushed the smoke and we stood to leave.

When Roman threw the punch, he brought it up from the balls of his feet right through my gut and into the concave hollow of my chest. I bent forward, holding my heart and belly with both hands. That's when he clocked me again. This time it was a hard right to the face and I stumbled backward over the side of the caboose.

I'd landed flat on my back with the wind knocked out of me. Trying to shout, but managing only to moan, I panicked and started flopping around like a fish on dry land. Finally, I caught a shallow breath. Then another, slightly deeper. A wave of relief washed over me. Hallelujah, I was going to live.

Roman came down off the caboose, walked over and kicked stones in my face. Then he dropped the pillowcase on my head, and for some reason that hurt more than his punches. He turned and walked toward our neighborhood. I was grateful he hadn't kicked me in the ribs.

I rolled onto my side, face leaking red onto the gray stones that lined the railroad tracks. I remember wishing a train would come by and chop off my head; anything to stop the throbbing in my skull. I feigned sleep, but even that was a con, as I was actually squinting. Through the squint, I saw Roman kicking rocks along the tracks, and a bull snake placidly watching me from under the caboose.

It had to be a mirage.

I closed my eyes, counted four beats and opened them. The snake watched me curiously—as if I were the one out of his element.

Four slow logrolls and we were face to face, his black tongue thrumming inches from my nose. I drew my arm down his body to a point below halfway; far enough to not get bitten, yet not so far that I'd damage his spine when lifting him from the ground. I slid a palm under his belly and scooped him gently, like scooping water.

"Come on Mr. Bull Snake," I said, and scooched out into the sun.

I tried to rise, but my skull seemed to float above my shoulders like a balloon on a string, so I rested in place a while, before wavering drunkenly to my feet.

The rumors were true; the snake was six feet long and fat as a Louisville Slugger. He was also surprisingly calm. He did not try to bite, nor even escape. Perhaps he knew what I'd come for. Or perhaps he knew that after causing so much harm to one species, I needed to even things out by helping another.

I directed him into the pillowcase tail first, but he latched his tail onto the lip of the sack. When I turned him face first, he dove in like the pillowcase was a gopher hole.

Even from a distance, the barbed wire fence with the V shaped brace loomed like an executioner, and my head was still pounding, so I climbed up into an empty boxcar and crashed out on the warm plank floor. Sometime later—with my face in the crook of an elbow and my free arm draped around the pillowcase—I was jolted awake, steel wheels rolling, boxcar rocking side to side. I rose slowly and walked to the open door, saw the entire southwest side of Chicago spread out and sparkling in late-afternoon sun.

The snake was breathing fine through the pillowcase, so I settled in a corner where I could see for miles and he could sleep on my lap. The train stopped at the western edge of the city, and I crushed us deeper into the corner, striving for invisibility.

We were outside Joliet when a thought crawled out from the swamp of my early adolescent, ophidian brain. The idea—that I might benefit from a little less persuasion and a lot more empathy—was new to me. And while that was many years ago, I've never forgotten it, and to this day still try to live by it.

The tracks rocked us light as a lullaby as we rode alongside great green corn fields and riverbeds long and fat as anacondas. I thought about removing the snake from the pillowcase, but being stuck in the bag so long, and my presence as a potential predator, might have caused him to abandon caution and slide out the open door.

Strains of flattened butter-yellow sun dripped down the distant horizon and vanished below the table as corn fields gave way to shimmering switchgrass and tall, stalky milkweed. And now a million flickering fireflies rose from the darkening earth, pulsing in dusky twilight, like pilots sent by some ancient snake god.

"They're here to guide us," I told the serpent.

Soon after dark, the train rolled to a stop behind a factory on a hill.

We were near a little farm town that I never learned the name of, but later determined was in Putnam County. I stepped from the car, pillowcase tight to the chest, Mr. Bull Snake a baby in my arms.

From where the sun had set I knew I was walking southeast, ushered by fireflies and the flickering bulbs of faraway farm porches and barns.

The night was clear and the rising moon bright as a torch as the fireflies blazed an amber ring around a perfect prairie. The meadow, a good two hundred times the size of our neighborhood wilderness, boasted the exact sort of sandy soil that bull snakes love.

There was even a slow flowing creek nearby.

"You behave yourself 'round here, Mr. Bull Snake," I said, "it's a better neighborhood than what you're used to." My legless friend ignored me entirely as I lifted him from the pillowcase, careful to keep both hands under the body.

It took mere seconds for the reptile to smell home with his black forked tongue, and now he flexed to be free. I gave him one last pet down the length of his spine, all the while wishing Roman were here to see this magnificent beast gain his discharge.

I counted four beats and loosened my grip. The snake slid through my fingers and into the brush, then flipped the tip of his tail like a goodbye wave as he disappeared.

A chorus of frog and insect calls blanketed me as I made my way toward the little farm town. I'd already vowed to stop reading all those goddamned persuasion books. Now I just needed to figure out how I was going to get back home without talking somebody into doing something they didn't really want to do.

The Loop   *Anthony Ball*

*"Chicago is not the most corrupt of cities. The state of New Jersey has a couple. Need we mention Nevada? Chicago, though, is the Big Daddy. Not more corrupt, just more theatrical, more colorful in its shadine*ss." — StudsTerkel

"Going to Chicago was like going out of the world." — Muddy Waters

When my good friend Vince first asked if I'd be interested in contributing a short story for this compilation, I instantly agreed. After all, I was born and bred in Chicago. No matter where I go in this world, I will die with Chicago concrete flowing through my veins. Writing a short piece about my hometown would be a piece of cake. But after a while, I started having second thoughts. I mean, everything that could be said about Chicago— from its origins, our quirky traditions (ketchup on hotdogs here is still a sin), the beauty of the city, the gang violence, the hard-working unions, the nepotism, our politicians, the segregation, the long history of police brutality, our sports teams— has already been written, and by those much more eloquent than I could ever hope to be.

So what to write about? What could I come up with that wouldn't sound like bragging, nor bore the living hell out of someone unfortunate enough to come across me ranting?

I didn't know and I got a case of writer's block. It was that way for months until that fateful night when there was a convergence of pandemic binging movies made in Chicago and a pint of Jameson (the preferred drink of every burnt-out detective and writer in almost every tv series and movie) in my living room.

I like to think that one thing we all have in common is a sense of pride when watching a tv series or movie made in our hometown. That sense of pride in seeing your city represented, knowing the scenery, having been to some of the locations, and for me, the nostalgia. At first, I watched *Primal Fear*, then it was *Ferris Bueller's Day Off*, and then *The Untouchables*, then *Cooley High*, and finally, *The Blues Brothers*.

Now, I've seen the aforementioned *Blues Brothers* literally hundreds of times before that last viewing, but it was in the quest for motivation that it really hit me in a different way—the sense of nostalgia, that feeling of 1980s Chicago.

There's a scene in *The Blues Brothers* where Jake and Elwood have just left the nunnery and are going back to Elwood's transient hotel room downtown. That scene takes them past State Street and what was once the old Loop. That scene means everything to me. Bear with me, I'll explain shortly.

Back in the '80s, Chicago was an entirely different animal than the one it is now. I won't get into the whole are things better now than they were then or try to compare and contrast the different decades. None of that, but what I will do is try to explain what it was like to be a kid here during that time and how the Loop was one of the most magical places on Earth.

Now please don't take "magical" as naivety. The ills of this city were there then just like they are now, I was just too young to realize or appreciate them. I mean, could you blame me? Back then we had one of the best arcades in the world (the Treasure Chest), some of the most beautiful lakefront scenery, and our famous Maxwell Polish sausages and grilled onions that you could literally smell miles away on a good day. Especially on the CTA, although when you rode the #8 Halsted bus, you couldn't be sure if it was the onions or body odor you were smelling.

The Chicago Transit Authority, our public transportation system, back then was absolutely terrible and wonderful at the same time. The fares were affordable, but you could wait for over an hour for a bus, and once you got it, it was a crapshoot as to if it would be too hot or too cold, if your window could open or if it was broken and swung open forcefully with every turn (if you could get a seat), if it wasn't packed from front to rear with working class people and pickpockets alike. The trains were an entirely different world. Vendors selling everything from candy to telephone cords to bootleg movies to powdered milk and all things in between. That would have been enough but you still had to deal with the con men with their three-card monte and shell games. If you were lucky, you would get the occasional aspiring rappers whose requests for donations were much more suggestion than solicitation.

But the CTA had one truly good, some would say great, thing about it back then: the SUPER TRANSFER. That magical little slip of paper bought on busses and trains gave you the ability to go anywhere in the city for one fare, all day on Sundays. It was definitely many a young person's path to escape whatever segregated neighborhood they lived in. For me, it was a way to get off of the Southwest side. A way to get away from all of the poverty, crime, depression, and the other bullshit that was always lurking around.

My friends and I would branch out all over the city, but the one place that was almost like a mecca for the 80s kids was the Loop.

I had always heard of Time's Square. Who hadn't heard of it or hadn't seen that mythical place depicted in New York set movies and tv shows? I could only imagine what that place was like, but one thing I knew for sure was that the Loop was our Time's Square. As good, if not better, than the real thing.

And this takes us back to *The Blues Brothers* movie. That scene where Jake and Elwood were going back to the hotel room took them past old State Street, that beautiful, neon, grimy, crowded main street of the Loop, the main part of our downtown area, the popular name for the business district located south of the main stem of the Chicago River. Back then, it had everything you could want. Department stores like Sears, Montgomery Wards, and Woolworths. The biggest and most awesome video arcade in the Midwest, the beforementioned Treasure Chest. There was the gaudy tourism shop on the corner of Washington and State Street, as well as the pawnshops and magazine stands up and down the main strip. The smelly Greyhound bus station across from the Daley Center was an entire world unto itself.

The atmosphere was a weird mix of electric and very laid back. You had the inner-city crowd mingling with suburbanites and nuclear families there for their weekend excursions. It truly was where you got to see almost every walk of life, every kind of person that you could imagine. There was something for everyone there during those years. From the name brand department stores to the low-key bodega shops off of the main strip, it was a wonderland. We had the world-famous blues and jazz festivals, the Taste of Chicago food fair, there was the Sears Tower, the brand new Thompson Center, the Carson Pirie Scott flagship store, but the main attraction for a poor kid with just a few bucks in his pocket was the old movie theaters. Oh my goodness, those old theaters!

Back when theaters had double and triple features, you could go to the movies all day for about four bucks. Each theater had its own identity, for better or for worse. There was The Woods, which was mostly known for horror and grindhouse movies, as well as for a lot of drunk people in the audience. McVickers and the Oriental were the best for seeing the old school kung fu movies. The Oriental was best known for having the stickiest floors known to man, and you had to constantly move your feet so that a rat wouldn't run across them (there's an urban legend about a woman having a heart attack at the Oriental after a rat jumped out of her popcorn). On the fancier end of the spectrum, there was the State and Lake and the Chicago Theaters. Those were where you went when you wanted to see the brand new, big feature movies. The Chicago used to be able to house a thousand people for a showing at full capacity—state-of-the-art sound system, minimal people yelling at the screens, and no sticky floors or claustrophobic feeling.

Located directly across the street, on the southwest corner of State and Randolph, was a sketchy, cheap rip off of White Castle named King Castle. Think of McDowell's in *Coming to America* and you'll get the idea. I remember it well because it was responsible for my poor mother having to drag her violently ill baby boy out of the first showing of *Flash Gordon* at the Chicago, and the transit system being what it was at the time didn't make things any easier.

My friends and I were able to hang out from the afternoon to sundown on about ten bucks apiece. If we were able to somehow come up on twenty bucks, we were kings because we got all of the above, plus we were able to come home with some sort of snack and a lot of comic books. I know that just about everyone thinks their childhood was the best, but it was truly a good time to come up here.

Chicago has changed a lot. There has been massive rezoning and gentrification. There was a time when you couldn't walk around in what are the more modern areas now. Some areas are completely unrecognizable from what they were decades ago. This city has had a massive facelift but a lot of the underlying problems, as well as a whole slew of new ones, are right underneath the surface. As I said earlier, I'm not trying to debate if things are better or worse now or to compare and contrast the decades, but I will say that I believe that my nostalgia for old Chicago and the Loop in the mid-70s through the 80s might be the best nostalgia going.

19th Street Sueños *Lorena Ornelas*

Feb 9, 2021 Nash and Fairy Games

6th floor, bare and abandoned: Champion Video. Rare velvet Lilly games, tartans and crepe paper—quarter century clan gatherings. Game show style for the new generations; dead language Lilly cards for the still here generation.

Feb 7, 2021 Grabby Jesus

Dinner and play—full lights and living statues. Huntress Diana and Wise Siddhartha cavorting… Excitement or Fear?

Lean young Jesus skipping down the aisles, gentle in his words, places his hand down the front of my shirt.

"May I?" He asks.

"No," I demand.

Jan 7, 2021 Bob Dole's Girlfriend

Bob Dole in a wheelchair at O'Hare Airport surrounded: High Security. (Like the Bardot in Tunis.) Creeping on me, nearing me at every turn.

Hello.

New girls in Congress always wear chic Chanel Suits, Chanel Pearls, a new Chanel outfit for every day of the week.

Bob Dole standing, walking, greeted by security. Doors opened by strangers. Joan Lunden? Teotihuacan.

(Why is a girl from Pilsen dreaming of these people?)

Jan 2, 2021 Chinese Performers

Menar arm-in-arm. Missed flights, Burger King and pharmaceutical disclosure. Volunteered to join in a performance of voodoo and Chinese mystics.

Hallucinations, dreams while waking, dancing… writhing.

Jan 2, 2021 Chicago

Roommates cleaning between library aisles. Kathleen Turner arrives unexpectedly, visiting old friends or looking to take over our bedroom where small cots and plastic pools live. Cleaning empty food containers.

Too big a risk to hug or receive her.

Water splashes over clear utensils.

Right hand small ball, nail-gunned into skin, large bald man removes 5 iron nails.

19th Street Basement—dog needs a walk, but Patty won't do it. Dad stands in front of an unfinished wall and cannot finish my name.

Locker room, Lupe, I don't know who I am. She leaves to play squash.

Dec 12, 2020 I'm going to Guatemala

Orgy—like melting waffles, pancake bodies. Woman, Asian, shower, used towels. Hurry to wash before he comes home.

Dad in a floral print shirt, clean handsome, standing in the doorway.

"I'm going to Guatemala in order to see the world; you have to see the world."

March 19, 2017 Rosarios

My father going out for apples in bell bottoms.

Blue Island shops of glass display window—flesh eating reptiles, loose fleshless bodies advising me hiding behind rosary cases.

September 4 2016 Nepali

Nepali meditative yoga guru named Dipendra sits on a window ledge for hours in deep thought/ meditation. People fall in between a gap of 2 buildings trying to reach him, trying to reach his heights. Men who would otherwise commit suicide in a year, men who are lost—he is saving them from their Catholic karma.

She is a married (separated) child therapist. Terrible parents keep winning custody of children they hurt. She wakes a wing full of crying infants on her last day to irritate the caregivers who agree with the courts.

Walking in her new heels, she steps in a vent and her heel gets caught. Her old friend (looks like Channing Tatum) catches her before she falls on the ground and she is grateful that he was out running errands while his wife was at home tending to their newborn. She leans in his arm and asks about them as he opens the umbrella for shelter and smiles, beaming with urgency.

Dipendra waits on the ledge. It's been days since he ate; he hasn't thought about intimacy or rent in 10 years. On the ledge, his mind is a pool of water—obstinate and porous. The 5th man has jumped to his death that year trying to reach him; their curiosity and their commitment to change has led them to his center for Vedic medicine. Entrance is through a standing window that abuts a neighboring building; few can successfully wiggle and climb through. The portly man or woman has to slim down— it is not about weight loss or deprivation, but the shaking off of material objects & desires, consumption of every kind.

She has reached the limit of her loneliness and confesses to him that she has always loved him, her good friend. He smiles, downward glance and is silent. No one speaks for several minutes. She is on her way before a judge who asked for her deposition 3 months ago and now wants her to return to offer court testimony. She likes the judge but decides he's too favorable to repentant parents who only want their children back. The best interest reports are scathing and prolong therapeutic foster care, but the parents are represented by a powerful lobby with greased lawyers who cut their teeth in cousins mothers brothers family firms on LaSalle Street. The guardian ad items are objective third parties, their visits with the children in her care leave them flustered, inspired and beyond tears when they get home to type up their weekly reports.

He smiles again, wraps his tall arm around her and she doesn't care that he smells like foot powder. He says family is what he has longed for all his life, and that years of coming to terms with his abusive parents and the absence of love and warmth in his childhood have only made his decision to be a father and provider grow stronger. She is grateful for his friendship and is embarrassed that she's pined for him for over a decade. She's on LaSalle and Washington now, leans away to go but he pulls her back to him, kisses her lightly on the lips and wishes her luck.

She doesn't regret moving back to Chicago from Florida after the aftermath of the case involving the Ramirez siblings. The disaster of that clusterfuck was her training.

What she doesn't yet know is that he has killed his wife and the baby was stillborn. He has killed several women on weekend trips to Juárez where his Marine pals have made friends with small time Cartel flunkies.

Dipendra is waiting for him on the ledge.

April 11, 2016 King of the Squirrels

king of the squirrels
war paint
white thick brows
tornado
Cookie and I in a Humvee
open all the doors

Couplet   *Stuart Dybek*

"Let's meet in the Loop."

Come in on the train that at best approximates time, with what your mother's generation called a woman's magazine that you'll leave behind on the seat you had all to your own. Instead of reading, you'll say that you rode to a song in your mind. (*Night and Day* or maybe *My Funny Valentine.*)

There, to meet you at Union Station, he'll think he glimpsed your overnight bag, the one that looks like a remnant from a flying carpet, disappearing into the Friday night rush from work. Despite cell phones, the crowd seems connected only by smoke and grounded carrier pigeons and reckless messengers on bikes.

It's fall. Later, the L will clatter by a silent hotel full of the strangers who can make the couples in stories seem even more themselves. But for now, he's at the wrong track, watching for you, braced against an empty coin box for *Crain's Business News.* (Maybe *Time On My Hand* or *I Concentrate On You.*)

You'll come up behind him and ask, "Are you lost, little boy?"

Don't worry you're late.

He'll wait.

On Surgery   *Dorothy Lam Frey*

The patient is a 24-year-old schizophrenic man. Two and a half years ago, he was on the corner of 18th street and Halsted accusing other pedestrians of collaborating with the devil. A man wearing a ten-gallon hat and a pair of imitation alligator boots shot him point blank in the chest after the patient called him a whore. The bullet pierced through his heart and esophagus. An ambulance brought him to a Chicago area ER where the on-call trauma surgeon miraculously saved his life by sewing his heart back together. But he couldn't reconnect the esophagus. Instead, he sewed the end of the esophagus together like a sock and put a tube from his skin to his small intestines so that caregivers could pour food into him.

The patient tried to eat whenever he could. In the milliseconds that bullet ripped through his chest, he also lost the chance to savor a bite of juicy steak or to lick an ice cream cone. If he tried to eat, his esophageal pouch would become distended. With nowhere for the food to go, he would vomit violently and then aspirate the food particles.

He was admitted to the hospital with pneumonia, and the large orderly strapped all of his limbs to his bed. He yelled at the nurses and medical staff whenever they entered his room, which reeked strongly of his unbathed body. His chart read "Vital signs and physical exam refused" day after day. One night, the patient somehow convinced a developmentally delayed man walking by to loosen his restraints. The patient ran out of the hospital in his pajamas and broke into the car of a deliveryman who was dropping off a pizza for some OB residents on call. In the seven minutes that the driver was away from his car, the patient ate three large pizzas.

He collapsed ten feet from the hospital entrance with intense chest pain and respiratory distress. The pizza had burst through his esophagus into his thorax. The surgeons cleaned out the half-chewed pizza and then connected his colon with his esophagus so that he could have a conduit for eating. The surgery lasted fourteen hours, and when his post-operative pain is controlled and his staples are ready to come out, he will be discharged.

A good story, isn't it? Before I started medical school, people always warned me that I might become immune to my patients' trials, that they would become as commonplace as runny noses. Still, I entered medical school. My classmates and I spent our first year and a half in the classroom, where we learned about cells, anatomy, and hundreds of diseases named after physicians of another time. Then we graduated onto the clinics, where we now rotate through different services like internal medicine, psychiatry, and pediatrics. We work in teams consisting of a couple of students and resident physicians who all answer to an attending physician. Surgery is my first hospital rotation.

I'm not sure what I expected seeing patients to be like— to be injected into freeze-frame moments of people's lives, to feel sometimes as ineffectual against their pain as an extra-strength Tylenol. But as a single, twenty-three-year-old medical student, I now find myself in an ambiguous role. Barely an adult, I lack much of wisdom that comes from life experience. But now I'm expected to guide people through their difficult decisions or moments of loss. I feel like an imposter on life itself. Each night, I try to suppress the unrelenting feeling that I am neither smart enough nor kind enough for this field.

The patient is a seven-month-old boy with curly blond hair, green eyes, and a chubby physique that would seem to rule out any eating difficulties. But actually, he has not eaten by breast or bottle since one month of age. Instead, his mother places a tube down his nose to his stomach and pours in formula. His chart reports that he had severe gastroesophageal reflux, but his esophageal study, performed five months ago, was inconclusive. All that is sure is that the baby has a very weak swallow since he hasn't swallowed for the vast majority of his life. Still, the baby is scheduled for a fundoplication, a procedure to wrap the stomach around the gastroesophageal junction to prevent the acid from traveling up the esophagus.

When the surgeon and I enter the patient's room, the surgeon proposes that we postpone the surgery for three days and give the baby a trial period of regular eating.

"One hundred percent of tube-fed people have reflux," the surgeon says, sitting down on the turquoise armchair found in every patient room. Her light blue scrubs contrast with her fuchsia surgical cap. "Your son needs to learn how to swallow. Why don't we just let him try to drink from a bottle over the next couple of days?"

"I know that it just won't work." The mother's eyes are wide open. Her voice is direct and unwavering. "My son needs this fundoplication. He's a very sick little boy. I have family that has come from out of town expecting that my baby will have surgery." Her jaw is now clenched.

She looks oddly at home in the hospital setting, cleanly dressed in pressed linen. Her short red hair is meticulously styled. I am bothered by this woman's eerie familiarity with surgical jargon and her determination that her baby undergo an operation that he may not even need. I can't shake this feeling that this mother has Munchausen's syndrome by proxy, a psychiatric disease where a caregiver tries to gain attention by faking her child's illness. Later, I learn that a fundoplication is not a minor procedure; one to two children a year die from complications from this surgery at this hospital.

"OK." The doctor agrees to do the operation, but leaves the caveat, "What if your child is the 1 in 1,000 chance that something goes wrong?"

The mother nods obligatorily, but half her mouth arcs upward in a knowing smirk. She seems satisfied with the outcome of this conversation.

The baby is taken to the operating room. My eyes are nodding off as we near the end of the laparoscopy. Three hours have passed, and I have only observed, not once touching a surgical tool. As the fellow ties the last knot, the metal rod he is using slips, and the abdomen fills with dark blood. The surgeons cannot control the bleeding through these tiny incisions.

"Oh my god," the attending surgeon screams. "We're in the pericardium." She grabs the knife and converts to an open procedure, carving a line down the baby's small belly. As this is occurring, the anesthetic is wearing off, and the baby begins to move and cry.

Luckily, we are not in the pericardium, the sac that encases the heart, but have only lacerated the hepatic vein, close to the inferior vena cava. The fellow stops the bleeding, but only after the baby has lost one-third of his blood.

When the surgery is finished and the baby remains stable, I am angry at this mother for putting her baby through a possibly unnecessary procedure. I review his chart again. The baby had multiple documented episodes of gastroesophageal reflux. He has two sisters, ages three and six. If his mother did have Munchausen by proxy, her two daughters would probably have extensive medical records also. They don't. Maybe the child did need the surgery. Maybe the mother wanted it scheduled that afternoon because it was the only time she would have someone to stay with her daughters.

I never know when to trust my instinctual reactions to mothers, not being one myself and thus not knowing how I would react in certain circumstances. At times, when I see these women whose main goal is to ensure happiness and health for their children, I am envious; they have a mission so concrete and well-defined. Such a lifestyle might be years or even decades down the road for me. Now that I find myself thrust into others' lives, I wonder if I have any knowledge to offer at this point in my life.

It is 5:30 AM, two days after the baby's surgery, and I have just examined him and written a note on his status. My surgical resident Steve asks, "How is he doing?"

"Fine," I reply. "He drank 200 cc of formula by mouth yesterday."

He snaps back, "That's how you present a patient? You haven't even told me who the patient is, his past medical history, his surgery, why he needed the surgery, and his symptoms this morning. Your inability to present tells me that you are not thinking properly."

I tell myself, in order to justify my mess-up, that I had written all of that information in the chart and that I didn't know he wanted a formal presentation. At home, I write in my journal, "As medical students, we are Seminole alligators that always lose to wrestlers. They know that we have weak jaw muscles, and if they just hold our mouths shut, they win. They can yell at us for lost charts, misspelling laparoscopic, cutting sutures too long, too short, not fast enough because our grades depend on their evaluations in this swamp."

The patient is a seven-year-old boy with a genetic disease called tubular sclerosis. Last year, he was also found to have an astrocytoma, a type of brain tumor. His black hair is sloppily cut, his huge yellow teeth protrude in every direction, and his eyes seem enormous against the backdrop of his gaunt face.

His legs are the same thickness as my wrists from his ankles to his groin, flexed into his body like a fetus. His eyes twitch from side to side like a typewriter because his brain can no longer control their movement.

Physically frail and developmentally delayed, he lies in bed alone all day. His mother, an undocumented immigrant, refuses to enter the hospital. His door is the only one in the hall that stays open all day and night. The television, always on, is tuned to the Cartoon Network.

The doctor wants to place a tube from his skin to his stomach so that he can receive supplemental feedings. He must phone his mother for permission since she's never at the hospital. And when I picture his mother on the other side of the phone call, all I feel is sympathy.

It is 4 AM on Sunday morning, and we just got out of an emergency appendectomy. My resident Steve and I are called to the ICU because one of our patients has a heart rate of 160. He flips his floppy blond hair to the other side, hands me the EKG, and tells me to interpret it. I begin talking about its rate, rhythm, and whether the p waves look regular, as I try to buy myself time using a methodical approach to EKGs that some 3rd year medical student taught me.

Steve cuts me off and asks for the diagnosis. I feel even smaller now as Steve nears me with his booming height and girth. I admit that I don't know; the EKG looks to me like a scribbling by the artist Cy Twombly. He says to me, "Doctor, your patient is dying! What are you going to do?" The truth is that the patient is not dying, not even in any distress, and can hear everything we say.

Steve holds out a ten-dollar bill. "Got any change?" he asks. The spangled moles on his face seem even more visible in the fluorescent light of the ICU.

"I don't think so."

"Mind going to the store and buying me some Cokes?"

"Well, umm."

"Are you tired? You look tired."

"No. I'm not. I'm fine." The truth is that I've been awake for twenty-three hours, and I'm not as alert as I could be. I dig through my backpack and find a dollar. "Do you want a Pepsi from the machine?"

"Yeah, I'll take the Pepsi, but I still want the Coke. A twelve pack—ice cold."

I search my mind for a good reason why I couldn't go, but I realize that given my exhaustion and my earlier screw-up, anything said would be unintelligible. I give up and go to the store.

It's forty degrees outside, and all I am wearing are my thin green scrubs. The parking lot is deserted, hazily lit by tall streetlamps, and my car is a quarter of a mile away in the employee section. Off in the distance, I can see some teenagers loitering and a bearded homeless man sleeping on the sidewalk. I am on high alert, remembering the fate of another medical student who was robbed, kidnapped, and then shot in the back of his head. Angry with myself for not standing up to my resident, I remind myself that my surgery grade is not worth my life.

When I return, Steve is asleep at the nurses' desk. I set the Coke next to him and go to sleep in the call room. I wake up forty minutes later to a page that we have started rounding. As we run from patient to patient, he never mentions the soda. He says, "You know, this was an easy night of call. We operated only once, and you even got some sleep."

The patient is a non-communicative 45-year-old woman who has been in the nursing home section of the hospital since her brain injury from a skydiving accident nineteen years ago. An abscess has now formed in the skin fold under her breast, and the nurse called the surgeons to remove it.

We cannot tell whether she is awake or asleep. Every breath vibrates like a snore. Her mouth is open with thick white drool dripping from its corner. Her eyelids are parted with her eyeballs rolled upward.

"She was a pilot," the patient's mother tells us. "Did you see the table?" She points to the hard-to-miss homemade shrine next to the patient's bed. There is a framed photograph of a woman with brown curly hair, wide-spaced eyes, and apricot-colored cheeks. An arrangement of purple and blue silk flowers in a copper tin and cards saying things like "We will never forget" occupy the rest of the coffee table.

The patient's mother, a woman in her late sixties with a helmet of hair and an upper back that hunches forward, visits daily. "I gave up hope that she'd come back years ago. Now I love the angel that she is." She sweeps the patient's oily hair from her forehead. "She's still beautiful."

"Can you imagine?" one of the other medical students says. "She lost everything in a matter of minutes."

But the patient's history isn't what bothers us. Twice a day, the other students and I come to change her wound dressing. One of us retracts her arm, another separates the folds of fat, and the last pulls and replaces the yards of gauze crammed into the seven-centimeter incision. The patient tries to fight us, but she has no muscle tone and cannot speak. We try to comfort her by talking to her and explaining what we are doing, but the only way to provoke her is with physical pain. This is what bothers us.

The patient is a fourteen-year-old in active labor. Her young face, framed by dark box braids, seems out of place atop her pregnant body. When I ask how she is doing, she replies, "Contraction-y," a clever play-on-words for an eighth grader. The intern tells her that we will give her a medicine to speed along her labor. The patient says, "I know. I've been reading. Pitocin."

She is correct. I imagine that she is the enthusiastic one in class, that one day she could solve integrals in her head effortlessly, if she had been born into a different society. She delivers an eight-pound, energetic boy while her mother with anxious eyebrows holds her hand. She tells me that she too wants to be a doctor. I really hope she becomes one.

The patient is a brain dead, 23-year-old male organ donor. When I enter the operating room, five surgeons and two scrub nurses surround the patient. He has a single midline incision stretching from his neck to his pubis, and there is an arc of staples across the side of his shaved head. The doctors swirl around the patient, switch places, and filter in and out of the room, the door of which is left uncharacteristically wide open. They move expeditiously, without any hint of frantic or wasted movement. They are so familiar with one another's actions that they do not have to say a word.

This, I think at the moment, is the pinnacle of human achievement, the ability of half a dozen surgeons to work so seamlessly and efficiently. The patient's heart and lungs are still pink— a perfect anatomical illustration. In many ways, he is the healthiest patient I've ever seen on the surgery table. He is also my first dead patient since my cadaver in anatomy class.

The head surgeon clamps his aorta, and within seconds, the liver and small intestines turn from pink to a yellowish tan, just like our cadavers. Two surgeons leave with his lungs and heart in a cooler. New surgeons enter to take his liver, kidneys, and pancreas. "What could this 23-year-old have done to deserve a side swipe to the head on a Tuesday night?" the kidney surgeon

215

wonders. The number of surgeons thin as the patient's body cavity becomes hollow. He is cold now.

I have seen the insides of a Vietnam vet who presented with a perforated bowel and an abdomen stretched with air. This is the man who was always so polite during 6 AM rounds, calling the other students and myself "doctor" and thanking us every day. Four weeks later, I see a man begging at the intersection of Division and I-95. I recognize his combination of blue eyes, gray brows, and a poorly trimmed moustache. It is eighty-five degrees outside, and the sun is directly overhead. His forehead is smudged with dirt, and I think I can see wavy lines of body odor rising from under his flannel shirt. Our eyes meet during the twelve seconds it takes me to place the face. He walks towards my car as if I were beckoning him with a quarter, but I hide my face from him as I wait out that ridiculously long light. I can't let him know that I have seen him at his most vulnerable, both as the naked man on the surgery table and as the relentless vagabond. Maybe I can't accept that I witness some people at their absolute lowest.

I try to enumerate the differences between my resident Steve and me because in five years, I don't want to be like him. But frighteningly, I can't think of many distinctions. I attempt to picture what his life is like when he's not in scrubs. His wife's daily routine, I imagine, revolves around Steve and his future prestige as a surgeon. I bet she doesn't work, spends her day at the gym, and cooks her husband a gourmet meal each night. But I am partly wrong; although she brings him homemade beef stew one day at the hospital, she isn't glamorous, hiding her heavyset thighs under sweatpants. As I watch them eat their lunch together, their attentiveness to each other, I feel something that I never thought I would feel towards Steve— jealousy.

My attending specializes in urology, which until recently was a very male-dominated surgical field. I calculate that he is about seventy based on where he was when Kennedy was shot. His gray hair and the way he makes me feel like a seventh grade girl confirm that he is from a different era. When we walk through the hospital, he often has to stop to pull up his scrub pants since his waistline exceeds his hips by about twelve inches. Still, he warns me not to become fat.

When I say I need to attend a lecture, he replies, "Whatever blows air up your skirt," and when we pass by attractive female drug representatives, he says, "Beautiful women have it easy. They just need to find someone to feed them." He knows; he's had four wives.

It is the morning of our surgery final, and students are not required to come into the hospital today, except for me. My attending expects me to show up despite his being well aware of our test this afternoon. When I arrive at his office, there are no patients. Instead, he gives me a surprise hour and a half oral exam on urology, a subject I have not been studying since our test is on general surgery. Every answer I give is wrong. He shakes his head and tells me to go study. My evaluation will reflect my poor fund of knowledge.

I leave his office and go to the bathroom where I cry like a misunderstood teenager. Exhausted and frustrated, I cannot concentrate during the test. This is the end of my surgery rotation. I have worked so hard and seen so much, yet it was not enough.

All I Saw Was a Dead Man
Jason Witherow

The job was hard. Driving the ambulances back and forth. Caring for people on the worst day of their lives. 12 hour shifts for nine bucks an hour, and after a year and a half of it, I was done. Burnt out. A thankless job when you look at it. People put life and limb on the line to save others. You make a pittance and you're expected to take shit and enjoy it. Others really love the life. It's a lot of glory. Though, some nights, like my last night, leave you with emotions you just can't forget.

When you work on an ambulance you work in pairs. One EMT, one Paramedic. I got to work with Captain Kent. One of those true Americans: enlisted in the Army during Vietnam, afterwards he bought a farm outside Chicago. He owned and trained therapy animals for veterans, and whenever he could, he would remind everyone about the Second Amendment. He wore cowboy clothes all the time. Everyone at the station called him "Walker, Texas Medic" behind his back.

It was Captain Kent and I driving around for the night. A full moon was out. We were at the beginning of our shift, and we could talk to each other without getting on each other's nerves.

"Full moon tonight."

"Yup," he said in his gruff Texan accent, "we got our work cut out for us, Stackhouse."

I always tried to lighten the mood with a joke,

"Reckon we'll get a call on a werewolf tonight?"

"Ain't no such thing as werewolves, Stackhouse. Chupacabras, on the other hand…"

We laughed. Minutes later we got dispatched to a two-car collision outside the city. The county cops declared the scene a mass casualty incident before the ambulance or fire department got there. Whenever a situation is declared an MCI, it doesn't mean a bunch of people died. It means that it is going to be a lot of work to help the people involved. I turned on the lights and sirens and started driving. It was 30 minutes away and we were the closest unit to the scene. The fire department was 45 minutes out.

There was one vehicle that barely looked damaged. It was an old beater of a truck—a 1980's Ford. Back in those days, cars had all steel bodies and frames. When they crashed, they didn't crumble like the cars made today. When a steel body vehicle crashes, it plows. The truck looked empty, but then we saw the rest of the scene.

The police were right to call it a mass casualty incident. There were scraps of aluminum and gore splattered across the highway. The other car was destroyed. The only intact occupant was the driver, safe behind the wheel. Everything else was sheared off, even the rear driver's side seat.

I parked the ambulance on the side of oncoming traffic so no one made our day harder. There were two deputies. They couldn't do much. One was walking around the scene with a clear plastic bag filled with blood and meat. The other was trying to get to the man in the car. Captain and I went to the destroyed car and realized we needed rescue tools to extract the man. I covered him with a tarp, so he wouldn't get hurt when the glass started flying, also so he didn't see the senseless carnage of his friends or family.

When the firefighters arrived, they started vehicle extrication. I was the smallest person on the scene, so I was the one who held the man's neck in place while the firefighters cut through the mangled door with a sawzall. The man became conscious when the saw revved up. He started to move, and I had to inform him, with the phrase we always use:

"Sir, you've been in an accident and we need you to stay still while we get you out, okay?"

"My family, how's my family," the man asked.

"We are doing everything we can," I lied. We always say that, even if there's nothing you *can* do. It's our job to keep them calm and get them to the hospital, but not explicitly lie to them.

After 20 minutes of holding the man's head in place while he dozed in and out of consciousness, my hands were cramping. Another smallish firefighter came in to take my place.

Captain Kent was with the deputies cleaning up the gore. I walked up to him rubbing my hands and spoke to the Captain.

"Hey Cap, we gotta look for the driver of the other vehicle."

Captain shot me a glance. It wasn't my place to tell him what to do. He knew picking up gore wasn't as important as finding another survivor.

"Stackhouse, take a look in the truck and see where you think he went."

I walked over to the driver's side door of the truck. The stench of alcohol hit me like smelling salts. The windshield had a circular hole the size of a large man. He was launched. I reached in the truck to pull the keys out, and put the emergency brake on.

I went over to the Captain and told him, "The driver was drunk and he had to have been launched into the trees across the way."

"I thought so."

"Should we go see if he's over there," I asked.

Captain Walker let out a big sigh. He handed his bag of body parts to the nearby deputy. "Reckon we ought to."

I had the Captain's medic bag ready. I handed him a flashlight from the side pocket, grabbed mine, and we headed across the highway to the trees. The Captain was walking ahead of me. Unlike me, he wasn't weighed down by a medic bag. We saw some blood on the ground and a trail of it leading away from the road. The drunk man was launched 70 feet, survived the crash, and tried to crawl away.

We followed the trail, me trying to catch up to the Captain. By the time I reached him, he was kneeled over a body that was covered in blood-soaked denim. I could smell the booze.

Captain Kent had his gloved hand on the man's neck. There was so much blood and it was so dark from the tree cover. He held his finger over the man's neck for 30 seconds, per protocol. Then Captain Kent looked up at me and shook his head. The Captain got up to leave, and as he moved I saw the man's chest move slightly.

"Captain, I think he's brea—"

"He's ain't got no pulse and we need to take the man in the other car to the hospital. Let's go, Stackhouse." He spoke in a way I hadn't heard since I last pissed him off a few months ago.

"Cap'n we might be able to save hi—"

"Jason. We are short on men, and supplies. We follow the MCI protocol, and now we take care of the living. Is that clear?"

He'd never called me by my real name before. I nodded and said, "Yes, Sir."

"Good, now grab the spine board and the stretcher."

We let the cops know there's a dead guy in the woods. The firefighters got the other man out of his car after a monumental effort. We loaded him up in the back of the ambulance. I drove toward the hospital while Captain Kent monitored the patient's vitals. The patient regained consciousness and spoke to us.

"My family, how's my family?"

"They are doing everything they can, we got to make sure you're alright. Can you tell me your family's names?"

"My uh, my son, Jimmy. My daughter, Emily. My wife, Stacey. God, please tell me they're okay?"

"We are taking care of you now, sir, we need you to calm—"

"Stacey, she's pregnant, oh god, is the baby alright?"

I looked in the rear-view mirror to see the Captain staring back.

"They are doing everything they can right now," the Captain said.

We arrived at the hospital and got him unloaded and into the emergency room. It was over for us. There was an uneasy calm, and I got to cleaning the ambulance for our next call. It is usually the best time of the day depending on the shift. No matter how bad the previous patient was, picking up used bags of saline, bandage packaging and wiping up body fluids is, by far, the least stressful thing to do. Like monks raking a rock garden, I could zen out and mentally prepare for the next call. Solitude before the next storm.

The fire engine from the scene pulled up next to the ambulance. Captain Kent went up to the fire truck window and spoke to the Fire Captain. This particular Fire Captain was the head honcho for us First Responders. The Godfather. He taught you everything you needed to know. He helped you get a good job, and he kept everyone in the fire department and ambulance companies in check. This was a mob meeting.

I finished cleaning, closed the rear doors and saw Captain Kent with the Fire Captain standing next to me. As soon as I saw him, the Fire Captain asked me, "What did you see in the woods tonight, son?"

"We saw the driver of the truck, I thought he might've been alive but—"

"I'm going to ask you one more time," the Fire Captain said, and held a pregnant pause, "what did you see in the woods?"

"All I saw was a dead man, sir."

"You're sure?"

"Yes sir, it will be in the report."

"Good man, good man."

The Fire Captain put his hand on my shoulder, walked back to his engine, and drove off. It was just Captain Kent and I, sitting on the rear bumper of the ambulance. We were looking at the moonlit doors of the ER bay. I took a deep breath. I was lightheaded, aware of my surroundings. There but not present, I couldn't hear the hustle and bustle of the busy hospital right in front of me, just muffled noises, the clear sound of my heart pounding and my deep shaky breathing. The start of my shift and I was already mentally done.

"Five people dead, sir," I said. I wasn't sure what else to say. "Good job," or "You did well," those platitudes don't sound right on calls like this.

"No, Jason. Six. No one is gonna come back from something like that." He lit up a Swisher Sweet and gave pause.

"I don't think I could do something like that again, sir."

Captain Kent offered me a puff of his cigarillo.

"I don't think you should."

I took a long drag.

I Burn Chicago *Vincent Francone*

There's the moment before we wake. That is when this is set, though it truly begins in 1871 in October around half past eight when people should know better than to be playing cards in a barn full of straw, though there's no stopping the game so long as there is strong drink, and is that Patrick O'Leary himself at the table doing his best to win back his family's security? Is that him thoughtlessly knocking over a lantern, unable to ever admit as much to Catherine, heaping blame on a blameless cow? And is it not the cow who'll bear the brunt of the myth to this day and probably for the rest of eternity, or the rest of Chicago, which now extends beyond the river and 1871's meager confines of what we see today as a world class city. That poor cow whose fate was to be no different than the cattle in the nearby stockyards but who suffers humiliation still as the scapegoat for the greatest disaster to hit the town, Thompson, Capone, Hinky Dink, Bathhouse, (Richard J. and Richie M.) Daley, and Rahm doing their utmost to top the blaze. But today that cow has returned to witness Chicago's expansion, marvel along with tourists on the architecture tour, take the water taxi, check out Chagall's *American Windows* at the Art Institute, get suckered into visiting Navy Pier and frustrated at the lack of anything to do on that odd growth into Lake Michigan, stroll through Streeterville, tire of the Mag Mile, catch the Red Line to Uptown for some slam poetry at the Green Mill, suffer some inclement weather and legs made unsteady by alcohol, consider vegan eats in

Andersonville and opt instead for simple grazing in Berger Park, eventually make it to the furthest northeast neighborhood before one abandons ship for Evanston. And in that area the cow will find me, born 99 years and eight months after the fire, writing this in the wee small hours in which this tale is set. The cow settles next to me, tired from a day of sightseeing, not sure what it'll do tomorrow, though it has one lucid thought before sinking back into the ether: Please, good man, convey this message to any who you can reach— I was not shy when milked and kicked over no damn lantern, but if I could go back I'd certainly start the fire, now that I see what good it did, now that things are prettier and wider and stronger, and now that there's more to do, for the Chicago of then was a miserable place for man, woman, and beast alike, and whatever malice, corruption, poverty, or disgrace you know can't hold a candle to the past, however hard you people insist on trying. Goodnight.

Meet the Contributors

Anne-Marie Akin never wrote a damn thing until she moved up north to Chicago and got so cold she had to write just to keep warm. She is a songwriter for the National Lullaby Project and teaches at the Old Town School of Folk Music. Her prose and poetry have appeared in various journals and the anthologies *The Buddha Next Door* and *THEY SAID: An Anthology of Collaborative Work*. Anne-Marie creates music and literature experiences for very young children in the Bronzeville community. DuSable Lakeshore Drive is her favorite street in the world.

Gint Aras (Karolis Gintaras Žukauskas) has been trapped on planet earth since 1973. He's the author of the novels *Finding the Moon in Sugar* and *The Fugue*, and a memoir, *Relief by Execution: A Visit to Mauthausen*. Raised in Cicero, he spent the weekends of his youth in Gage and Marquette Park. Learn more at http://gint-aras.com.

Vimi Bajaj is a writer and physician near the Chicago area. A graduate of the Bennington Writing Seminars, she is currently at work on a novel set in modern day India, "Vermilion," which won the 2020 Unpublished Competition for Literary Fiction. Her stories have been published in the *Bristol Short Story Prize Anthology*, *The Dr. TJ Eckleberg Review*, *Audible* and elsewhere.

Marc Baker moved to Chicago in 2014 and has apartment hopped across five neighborhoods in seven years. He currently resides in Wicker Park. Marc has self-published 2/3 of a speculative fiction trilogy, *Port*, that wonders what life would be like if teleportation existed. You can find links to his work and other random musings on his website. https://www.marcalanbaker1.wixsite.com/worldofport

Anthony Ball is an amateur comic book writer and editor. He is also a lifelong Chicagoan. An avid fan of the Bears, Cubs, Bulls, and Irish whiskey, he still takes on freelance writing assignments occasionally. Anthony lives on the southwest side of Chicago in the Auburn Gresham neighborhood.

After jumping around North America, Latin America, and Europe, **Ines Bellina** settled in Chicago. She is a co-author of *LGNSQ: Gentrification and Preservation in a Chicago Neighborhood* and has a byline in *Chicago Magazine, The A.V. Club, The Takeout,* and more. Follow her on Twitter at @ibwrites.

Robert Burkenhare lives in Uptown. He likes to write things that are difficult to classify. He has very strong opinions on what makes good art, all of which he hopes to share soon in a literary journal of his co-creation. Preferring the company of dogs and cats, he has never married, reproduced, or willingly lived with another human being.

Coleman fled from Oklahoma as a teen, stumbled as an undergraduate at Cornell University, and was arrested for opposing the war in Vietnam. Upon his release from prison, he resumed his studies in Ann Arbor, then disguised himself as various professionals in the alleys, lofts and high-rises of Chicago. He is the author of a memoir (*SPOKE*) and more than 40 plays. Visit his website at www.spokesinthewheel.com.

Stuart Dybek is the author of *The Coast of Chicago* and five other books of fiction, as well as two collections of poetry. His work is widely anthologized, and magazine publications have included *The New Yorker, Harpers, The Atlantic, Granta, Zoetrope, Ploughshares,* and *Poetry*. Dybek has received several literary awards including a MacArthur Foundation Fellowship.

Eileen Favorite was born in Mercy Hospital in Bronzeville and raised in the south suburbs with eight siblings. She's lived in a crooked two-flat in Lincoln Square since 1999, during which time she published a novel, *The Heroines* (Scribner), essays, flash, and a bit of poetry. She teaches at the School of the Art Institute of Chicago and the Graham School of Continuing Liberal and Professional Studies at the University of Chicago. Find out more about her at www.eileenfavorite.com.

Nick Francone is a Cubs fan who lives in the Western burbs of Chicago. In 1992 he started working in the Loop and still works downtown today. He currently resides with his girlfriend Nancy and their dog Rudy and cat Moose.

Vincent Francone was born in the southwest suburbs of Chicago, moved to the north side when he was in his early 20s, and has since lived in 17 apartments in the city. He's called Rogers Park home for 14 years, during which time he published a memoir (*Like a Dog*) and a collection of essays (*The Soft Lunacy*). Visit his website www.vincentfrancone.com to learn more.

Dorothy Lam Frey, a radiologist, moved to Chicago in 2005 for her medical training and has called it home ever since. She now resides with her husband and their two toddler daughters in a lively downtown apartment, while they patiently await completion of their gut-rehabbed two-flat in the Lincoln Square neighborhood. She is currently working on her first YA novel, *The Cyborg Project*. Visit her website dorothylamfrey.com.

Caitlin Garvey grew up in Oak Park, IL, and now lives in Edgewater with her wife and cat. Her memoir, *The Mourning Report,* is about losing her mother to cancer and collecting the stories of Oak Parkers and Chicagoans who played a role in her mother's care. Visit caitlinhogangarvey.com to learn more.

RL Gehringer grew up on the north side of Chicago and attended Chicago Public Schools. After high school, RL drove delivery vans and Yellow Cabs until a fateful day in 1977, when he talked his way into the computer industry. RL has two grown children and resides with his wife in Northern California. He can be reached at rlgehringer@gmail.com

Nestor "the Boss" Gomez was born in Guatemala and came to Chicago Uptown, undocumented, in the mid 80's. He told his first story at a Moth Story Slam in Chicago's North Center neighborhood to get over the stuttering that plagued his childhood. Since then, he has won more than 60

Moth Slams and several Grand Slams. He currently lives in Edgewater. To listen to Nestor's stories, to buy his ride sharing opus, *Your Driver Has Arrived*, and to learn more about Nestor, visit his web site: Nestorgomezstoryteller.com.

Adrienne Gunn is a writer, editor, and podcaster based in Chicago. She received an MFA in creative writing from the University of Oregon and is a contributing writer at *Chicago Magazine*. Her work has appeared in *McSweeney's, TriQuarterly, PANK*, and other literary journals. Adrienne's first solo show *Mother of the Year!* premiered and returned to sold out audiences. Visit her at www.adriennegunn.com.

Wayne Lerner is a retired healthcare executive. He was born in the Austin neighborhood and lived there through the riots until 1969. He has graduate degrees in health management and policy and currently serves on the board of a not-for-profit safety net hospital and teaches graduate students in health systems management. A lifelong Chicagoan and White Sox fan, he's published in professional journals many times and edited a book on a major hospital merger, but he has never achieved a dream he had while in high school and college to publish an original work of fiction... until now.

Joe Mallon was born on the South Side of Chicago, spending his early years in the Mt. Greenwood neighborhood. He grew up on Sacramento Ave., down the street from the Knights of Columbus Hall. He was lucky enough to live across from the Grand Trunk railroad line, where a strip of land (the prairie) between the tracks and street served as a field for baseball, football, hockey, and games the kids on the block invented. After the required post-college trek to Lincoln Park, he now lives in the Beverly neighborhood with his wife, Barb.

David Mathews earned his MA in Writing & Publishing at DePaul University. His work has been nominated for Best of the Net, a Pushcart, and he was a finalist in the Gwendolyn Brooks Open Mic Awards. His recent publications include *Midwestern Gothic, Eclectica Magazine, Endlessly Rocking*, an anthology honoring Walt Whitman, and *Belt Magazine's Rust Belt Chicago: An Anthology*. A lifelong Chicagoan who grew up on the Northwest side, David works as a Creative Writing Instructor at the Chicago High School for the Arts (ChiArts).

Dipika Mukherjee moved to Chicago from Shanghai in 2012. She is the author of the novels *Shambala Junction* and *Ode to Broken Things,* and the story collection, *Rules of Desire.* Her writing is included in *The Best Small Fictions 2019* and appears in *World Literature Today, Asia Literary Review, Del Sol Review, Chicago Quarterly Review, Newsweek, Los Angeles Review of Books, Hemispheres* and *Orion.* She teaches at StoryStudio Chicago and at the Graham School at University of Chicago. More at www.dipikamukherjee.com.

Tom Myers was born in Cleveland, went to college in central Illinois then moved to Chicago in the early 70s. After 28 years in the Navy, he returned to the Lakeside neighborhood of Chicago where he and Paul Teodo have collaborated on two novels, *PASTAMAN* and *Call Me Z.* They are currently working on a collection of short stories centered on Chicago's south side.

Steve Nelson lives and writes in the Edgewater neighborhood of Chicago and previously lived in Uptown. He earned his PhD in Creative Writing from the University of Wisconsin-Milwaukee and teaches at Concordia University Wisconsin. He has had stories and essays published in a number of journals and anthologies and is the author of *Teaching the Way: Using the Principles of "The Art of War" to Teach Composition.*

Lorena Ornelas was born and raised in Pilsen. She likes to help people and loves dogs.

Vojislav Pejović was born in 1972, in Titograd, former Yugoslavia, which, through a quirk of history, also means that he hails from Podgorica, Montenegro. He moved to Chicago in 2005. Once resident—and a lifelong fan—of Andersonville, he now lives in Evanston, IL. Both of his novels, *The Life and Death of Milan Junak* (Serbo-Croatian) and *American Sfumato* (English, Serbo-Croatian), were written in and around Chicago.

Joseph G. Peterson is the author of several works of fiction and poetry. His most recent novel, *The Rumphulus,* was published in 2020 by the University of Iowa Press, and his forthcoming novel, *Memorandum* *from the Iowa Cloud Appreciation Society*, will also be published by the University of Iowa Press in 2022. The Des Plaines River winds through the imaginary territory of many of his books. He currently lives with his family in Hyde Park on the southern shore of Lake Michigan.

Keith Peterson, a life-long Chicagoan, worked for most of his career in bookstores, new and used, and was the owner of Selected Works Used and Out of Print Books for many years. He is retired, and writes, takes photographs, reads, and tries to stay out of trouble.

Nancy Werking Poling's "write-what-you-know" efforts invariably return her to the years when she lived in Evanston and took the El to work in downtown Chicago. Her most recent book publications include *While Earth Still Speaks*, an environmental-themed novel, and *Before It Was Legal: a black-white marriage (1945-1987)*, a non-fiction biography.

Harry Quinn was born in Mt. Greenwood, a neighborhood most of the residents believe is the best in Chicago. He disagreed, moved to Lakeview in 1988 and has stayed there ever since. He expects to be priced out any day now, as he's reaching retirement age and Christ knows there's no money left for his pension. He used to write music reviews until music went to the dogs. Today, he is at work on a book of short stories, most of them set in bars and diners.

Christopher Sebela was born in Chicago and in his 25 years there, he never lived more than a few blocks from Broadway for some reason he can't figure out. Currently he works as a comic book writer who has put words in the mouths of Superman and Batman. He's published over a dozen creator-owned books, including *Crowded*, *Shanghai Red*, *Heartthrob*, *Dirtbag Rapture*, and *High Crimes*. He can be found at christophersebela.com.

Gary Slezak grew up on Chicago's southwest side and began writing plays in college. Most of his plays—*Malek's Dependents*, *Beat the Jester*, *Playhouse*, *Hurry Slowly* and *Cry Uncle*—expose the lives of Chicagoans for whom life is a glass half-full. Gary has lived in Marquette Park, Beverly, Hyde Park, Lincoln Park and Streeterville. He has worked in libraries at the University of Chicago and Northwestern University. For more, go to www.garyslezak.com.

Cajetan Sorich is a writer who grew up beside a soybean field in Illinois. She moved to Chicago at age 17 and lived in Humboldt Park for eight years. Caj's writing has been published by *Scapi Magazine, MAKE Literary Magazine, Queen City Writers, and Euphemism*. She's also an artist who performs with a group named VAIL and who choreographs the occasional music video.

Paul Teodo was born and raised on Chicago's south side. Son of a factory worker and owner of an Italian deli, Paul is a retired Healthcare exec. His last "tour of duty" was at a poverty-stricken Catholic hospital on Chicago's south side. He and his long-time friend Tom Myers have published two Chicago based books, *PASTAMAN* and *Call Me Z*, and are finalizing a soon-to-be-published book of short stories featuring tales from Chicago's south side.

A.L. Trellis lived on two different continents before moving to the United States, specifically the Edgewater neighborhood of Chicago.

Steve Trumpeter's fiction has appeared in *Southern Review, American Fiction, Chicago Quarterly Review, Salamander*, and others, and he was a finalist for the *Chicago Tribune*'s 2019 Nelson Algren Award. In 1996, he emigrated from Tennessee in order to earn a degree in fiction writing from Northwestern University. He has lived in the city proper for longer than he lived in the south, so now identifies as an official Chicagoan who believes that dibs claims are valid, but only for three days. He teaches at StoryStudio Chicago, and his writing, oil painting and music can be discovered at https://stevetrumpeter.com.

Cyn Vargas is a native Chicagoan, who grew up on the Northwest side, and still calls the city home. Cyn's short story collection, *On The Way*, (Curbside Splendor, 2015; 2nd Edition Tortoise Books 2021) received positive reviews from *Shelf Awareness, Library Journal, Heavy Feather Review, Newcity Lit, Hypertext Magazine, Necessary Fiction* and others. Her prose and essays have been published in the *Chicago Reader, Word Riot, Split Lip Magazine, Hypertext Magazine, Midnight Breakfast*, and elsewhere. Visit her website at www.cynvargas.com to learn more.

Jeremy T. Wilson has lived in Hyde Park, Lakeview, North Center, Wicker Park, and Logan Square. He is the author of the short story collection *Adult*

Teeth, published by independent Chicago press Tortoise Books. He is a former winner of the *Chicago Tribune's* Nelson Algren Award for Short Fiction and was recently named one of 30 Writers to watch by Chicago's Guild Literary Complex. He teaches creative writing at the Chicago High School for the Arts. Go to jeremytwilson.com to learn more.

S.L. Wisenberg's work appeared in *the New Yorker, the Sun, Ploughshares, Michigan Quarterly Review, the New England Review* and many other journals as well as anthologies. She is the author of an essay collection, *Holocaust Girls: History, Memory & Other Obsessions* (University of Nebraska Press); a chronicle, *The Adventures of Cancer Bitch* (Iowa), and a story collection, "The Sweetheart Is In" (Northwestern). She lives in Chicago, where she fights envy and despair, and edits *Another Chicago Magazine*.

Jason Witherow lived in Lincoln Square in his 20s and worked gigs around downtown Chicago, from getting fired and rehired by coked up civil rights lawyers, to data entry in strange basements beneath the city. He earned his Creative Writing degree at Roosevelt University. He travels the country with his wife Caitlin, his dog, his cat and his parrot. You can visit his website at jasonwriteweb.wordpress.com.

Rose Maria Woodson is a Lawndale girl. Although that particular time is no longer, she treasures her Lawndale like Atlantis, submerged, simmering in memory. She has been published in numerous journals, including *Revolute, Blue River, Oyez Review, Crack The Spine* and *Black Fork Review*. She has work forthcoming in *Litro, Glint* and *Cider Press Review*. She is the author of two chapbooks, *Skin Gin* and *The Ombre Of Absence*, as well as the mini-chapbook, *Dear Alfredo*. She holds an MA in creative writing from Northwestern University.

Acknowledgements

"Little Man" by Jeremy T. Wilson was previously published by *Stymie: A Journal of Sport, Games, and Literature.*

"Inherently Chaotic" by Adrienne Gunn appeared under a different title in *Chicago Magazine.*

Joseph G. Peterson's "Vargas" is excerpted from his book *Ninety-Nine Bottles*; "On the Way" is excerpted from Cyn Vargas's book of the same name; Nestor Gomez's story "Your Driver Has Arrived" comes from the book of the same name; "American Sfmuto" is excerpted from the book of the same name by Vojislav Pejović. All of these were published here with kind permission from Jerry Brennan Tortoise Books.

Wayne Lerner's "Welcome to the Bigs" appeared, under a different title, in the journal *Literate Apes*. They also published Paul Teodo and Tom Myer's "People Gotta Eat."

A longer version of Sandi Wisenberg's "CTA Journal" was published by the *Chicago Reader*.

"The Hierarchy of Grief" by Dipika Mukherjee was previously published in *Singapore Unbound* in recognition of the anniversary of the disappearance of Malaysian Airlines flight MH370.

"You Shall See the Face of God and Live" first appeared in *Little Fiction: Big Truths* and was amended to appear in Caitlin Garvey's book *The Mourning Report*.

Eileen Favorite's "Three Lunatic Misunderstandings of the Urban Midwest" was first published by *Essay Daily*.

Made in the USA
Las Vegas, NV
19 November 2021

34839437R00136